KNOWLEDGE AMONG MEN

ELEVEN ESSAYS ON SCIENCE, CULTURE, AND SOCIETY
COMMEMORATING THE 200TH ANNIVERSARY OF THE
BIRTH OF JAMES SMITHSON

INTRODUCTION BY S. DILLON RIPLEY
SECRETARY OF THE SMITHSONIAN INSTITUTION

PUBLISHED BY SIMON AND SCHUSTER, IN COOPERATION
WITH THE SMITHSONIAN INSTITUTION, WASHINGTON, D.C.

LIBRARY OF CONGRESS CATALOG CARD NUMBER: 66–19430
DESIGNED BY EVE METZ
MANUFACTURED IN THE UNITED STATES OF AMERICA
AMERICAN BOOK–STRATFORD PRESS, NEW YORK, N.Y.

Edited and with introductions
by PAUL H. OEHSER

CONTENTS

INTRODUCTION

S. DILLON RIPLEY

SECRETARY OF THE SMITHSONIAN INSTITUTION

MAN'S KNOWLEDGE has doubled in a lifetime. The complexity of the universe, of human history, of man's self-awareness severely tests our comprehension. Since the American people accepted the bequest of James Smithson the Institution bearing his name has been devoted to the advancement of knowledge and its appreciation by the citizen. On the two-hundredth anniversary of his birth a number of the world's leading scholars gathered to appraise man's knowledge. Their papers, collected in this volume, trace certain classic themes which are the foundations of knowledge.

They see man's knowledge as a vast fabric telling us as much about those who have created it as about the objects of their thought. If the extent of this knowledge is the hallmark of our civilization, the use to be made of it may be its crisis. Through understanding how knowledge has progressed and what it tells us of ourselves we may better know how it should be used to advance man's welfare.

The laws of the physical universe are somewhat parallel to those of the world of life and even to those of the realm of the mind. The evolution not simply of organisms but of galaxies, of cultures, and of individual personalities reveals some similarities. James Smithson enjoined the Institution to make these unities manifest: "the particle and the planet are subject to the same laws, and what is learned of the one will be known of the other." The essays in this volume bespeak a unity of knowledge which provides an avenue to understanding for us all, scientist and layman alike.

We must also understand how knowledge has its origin in experi-

7

ence and the course of thought. The scientist does not simply amass new bits of information like beads of glass on a string. The progress of knowledge depends upon a profound interplay among the structure of theory, the accumulation of evidence, and intuition. It is tempting always to dress out the same old notions with slight alterations responding to fashion more than fact. But we must avoid becoming fixed in our ideas. The best remedy for sterility of that kind is to seek nature in the fact, to employ all the senses in a direct encounter with the problem. This is one of the principal values of museums.

Many interesting problems are associated with the study of objects and the managing of collections. It is paradoxical that most people would rather read about objects than study them directly. In our system of education today we assume that one can be educated only by learning to read at least, if not to write. The use of the eyes, increasingly on the television screen, becomes all important. The assumption that truth can be learned, second hand, by reading what someone else has written, is all-pervasive. It dominates our thinking. It forms the foundation stone of our system of education. There is obviously a confusion here which becomes glossed over and unrecognized in our educational training. Rules may be printed out and learned by rote, but truth cannot be printed out, and probably not absorbed just by reading, and certainly not learned by rote.

In this pattern, this set of assumptions, the objects are left off, and those institutions which harbor collections of objects, as libraries do books, get left out also. It is a common postulate that a man can be educated to take his place in much of our professional society without ever being in contact with objects in the sense of learning through them or by working with them. Is there something degrading about objects? Does the touching of them and working with them imply something less than what an educated man, above all a scholar, would do? Does it imply a kind of illiteracy? If there is such an assumption, if someone who touches objects, who works with his hands is considered to be a common laborer, then there is something wrong. In our American way of life we tend to assume that everyone must now go to college in order to be happy, to have equal opportunity, to fit our ideal of the finished, the complete citizen. But if by going to college one grows away from objects, becomes a reader and not a toucher, then

8

there is something wrong, for there are many roads to insight and to the discovery of truths. What is clear is that in the pursuit of knowledge no road should be left unexplored.

Indeed there is a talent in being illiterate. For some people insight and learning derive from the sense of touch. Objects are documents to be read as much as the printed page. Many people and all children need to touch objects, assess their texture, not simply read about them, in order to learn. St. Peter's toe, a dinosaur bone in a museum, a live cow, a piece of sculpture, a stone ax; we have a need for objects. Through them the truth is seeking us out.

I sometimes think that people shrink from the attempt to learn from objects because one must give a little of oneself to the objects in the process. To study objects is more demanding than to read about them. To use them one must give a little, and how few of us like to do that. It is safer, less obligating merely to read and learn by rote. One can always put the book away and forget about it after the exam. How many social anthropologists or social psychologists of today have ever felt the tools, the axes, and the masks about which Malinowski and Boas wrote? Most of our social theory today is based on the written observations of anthropologists of a generation or two ago who worked with primitives, groups of isolated, illiterate yet enormously skilled people beautifully adapted to their way of life, people who had the talent to be illiterate, to work by touch, speech, and hearing to create complex and sophisticated cultures. I suspect that many of the best anthropologists of today have an almost unconscious yearning to touch objects, to hear chants, to savor cultures by *not* reading about them. They should come and look at the objects and the texts in the collections at least. These exist while many of the cultures that gave them life have vanished from the scene. These can be felt and touched, and, if you give a little, they can be made to teach something. There are certainly new truths to be derived from them. They are the testament, the original revelation. Colleges and universities should understand this and should include museum objects as a vital part of higher education. Objects are not an end in themselves to be fondled and cherished, but purely verbal people may come to mistake the representation of reality for reality itself.

The educator of today should recognize museum objects as much more than the static byproducts of past ages. The object may be approached again and again from differing points of view and be made to yield clues to biological or even cultural environments and their formative influences. These evidences may be transposed dynamically into systems which may be models for discerning future trends in environmental change, human ecology, and cultural patterns. The object is a catalyst enabling the museum to perform intellectual synthesis, helping to meet a need, particularly urgent in our time, to translate history into prediction.

Curiously enough, scholars do not always wish either to give of themselves or to search out and grasp the nettle of truth. Many scholars both in science and in the arts and humanities wish to join only the previously initiated few, an already chosen circle. Let a segment of art or a segment of science become fashionable, a discovery be made, and a welter of scholars will run, a veritable gaggle of geese, in search of crumbs of an original truth which can be mulled over, fragmented, and attenuated until they become mere chaff, echoes of a past act of discovery. There are graduate students today who are going into various abstract phases of molecular biology because it is safe, because they can get a job, and possibly a retirement plan, by refining segments of past discoveries, while the vast, unformed, incomprehensible truths of environmental biology elude us for lack of enough people willing to get their hands dirty.

In the field of art, history, and criticism the same can be true. Scholarship for scholarship's sake, too attenuated and refined, provoked Francis Taylor once to say, "The locust has flown away while we have been debating the morphology and iconography of his discarded shell."

It has been said over and over that now that our Federal Government has taken the decision to assault the massive problems of education in this country, it is up to the private foundations, who have in some instances pioneered, charted the way for present-day acceptance of this principle of Federal support, to pioneer anew. How can foundations help in the next stage, the stage that goes beyond providing an opportunity for education for everyone? The horse can be led to water but not made to drink. The equal opportunity is not enough.

People will not become educated unless they are interested, unless they have goals and a purpose, and above all interests. If the future for everyone is to include leisure, then objects come again onto the stage, interests, crafts, hobbies. Through the study of objects we can revive dormant skills and unconscious drives and urges that lie submerged in people as in what I have called the talent to be illiterate.

Furthermore we can study how best to interest people in things through programs and research in museums. Objects properly displayed and explained bring the visitor back time after time. Beyond this the visitor may enroll in classes to work behind the scenes with the materials themselves. We can study that elusive subliminal threshold of interest, of how to be interested in anything at all. For this the Smithsonian hopes to join hands with imaginative and pioneering foundations.

If the Smithsonian Institution has a motto, aside from the enigmatic and Sibylline "increase and diffusion of knowledge among men," it should be *the pursuit of the unfashionable by the unconventional.* This motto would not be unique. It should be shared by some of our greatest organizations devoted to basic research, the Rockefeller University and the Carnegie Institution, to take two illustrious names also associated with original philanthropy. But in its history the Smithsonian has always tried to do only what for various reasons other organizations or agencies were not doing, and to husband its resources of manpower toward the accomplishment of abstract and original study.

Let us hope that the venerableness of this Institution does not require us to accept Brancusi's suggestive statement that "when we are no longer young, we are already dead." To function we must not become set or rigid, but always receptive to new possibilities. To be creative in the arts or the sciences we must retain the direct apprehension of the environment, the external world. As Dubos has said, to retain this perception is the "surest approach to a true enlargement of human life." Let this indeed be our mission.

11

JEROME S. BRUNER

Jerome Seymour Bruner, American psychologist, was born in New York City on October 1, 1915. He earned his B.A. degree from Duke University in 1937 and his Ph.D. from Harvard in 1941.

During World War II, he worked on the analysis of propaganda and public opinion in the United States and later overseas for the Office of War Information, the Department of State, and the Supreme Headquarters Allied Expeditionary Force (SHAEF). Although his prewar work in psychology had been concerned mostly with perception and learning, his wartime experience led him increasingly into the field of social psychology, particularly the study of opinion.

Bruner returned to Harvard in 1945 as lecturer on psychology and was appointed Associate Professor in 1948 and Professor of Psychology in 1952. His interest returned increasingly to the nature of the processes underlying opinion formation and other social phenomena—perception, thought, learning, language. From 1950 to 1960 he directed an informal federation of researchers working on the nature of cognitive functioning—and then helped found, in 1960, the Center for Cognitive Studies at Harvard. Bruner was appointed a visiting member of the Institute for Advanced Study, Princeton, in 1951–52, a Guggenheim Fellow in 1955–56 at Cambridge University, and as Harvard's Bacon Professor at the University of Aix-en-Provence in the spring of 1965.

In the past few years Professor Bruner's interest in the intellectual processes has extended itself to the study of development in children, and with that has grown a parallel interest in the nature of the educational process. He has been engaged for most of the past year in the construction of an elementary school curriculum in social studies, based on conceptions set forth in some of his earlier studies.

He has published numerous books and articles on the nature of cognitive processes. Among his books are *A Study of Thinking* with Goodnow and Austin, *Opinion and Personality* with Smith and White, and *On Knowing: Essays for the Left Hand*. He was chairman of the Woods Hole Conference on Fundamental Processes in Education sponsored by the National Academy of Sciences in 1959, and from his report as chairman his book *The Process of Education* was derived. *Toward a Theory of Instruction* appeared early in 1966, bringing Mr. Bruner's educational ideas up to date. Also scheduled to appear in 1966 is *Studies in Cognitive Growth,* setting forth the research findings of the group working along with Mr. Bruner at the Center for Cognitive Studies at Harvard.

Bruner has served as a member of various advisory boards in and out of the Government. He has been a member of the President's Advisory Panel on Education and has served on committees advising the State Department, the United Nations, the Department of Defense, the National Science Foundation, and the National Institutes of Health. He was chairman of the Group on Education, Technology, and Training, studying educational problems in Africa. He has been on the editorial boards of *The Public Opinion* and *World Affairs,* has served as a Syndic of Harvard University Press and a member of the Advisory Board of Educational Testing Service, and at the present time is co-director of Educational Services Incorporated Social Studies Curriculum Project.

He has served in various capacities in the American Psychological Association, and most recently as President for 1964–65. In 1962 he received the Association's Distinguished Scientific Award. Professor Bruner is a founding member of the National Academy of Education, a Fellow of the American Academy of Arts and Sciences and of the American Association for the Advancement of Science, and Honorary Foreign Fellow of the Federation Suisse de Psychologie and honorary Officier de l'Instruction Publique of France.

The Perfectibility of Intellect

JEROME S. BRUNER

I SHALL CONCERN MYSELF in what follows with the vexed problem of the perfectibility of man's intellect. Let me consider the matter in the light of four constraints on the exercise of intellect. The first is the nature of knowing itself, as we observe it in intact human beings attempting to gain knowledge. The second derives from the evolution of intellect in primates, including man. The third constraint is imposed by the growth of intellect from childhood to such perfection as man may reach. The fourth has to do with the nature of knowledge as it becomes codified and organized in the society of learned men. It is too broad a task I have set for myself, but unavoidably so, for the question before us suffers distortion if its perspective is reduced. Better to risk the dangers of a rough sketch.

Let me confess that I, indeed any student of human intellect, can hardly pretend that what I say of the reach and range of human intellect is innocent of social, political, and moral consequences. For however one poses the problem whatever one finds must inevitably affect or at least question our conception of what is humanly possible in the cultivation of mind. The issue of the perfectibility of intellect stirs passionate debate. Beware those who urge that the debate is without purpose, that the results of scientific inquiry carry self-evident implications with them. For it is a debate that requires continual renewal lest our educational enterprise fail to fulfill its function either as an agency for empowering human minds or as a reflector of the values of the culture. What the student of human intellect can do is to refresh the debate with estimates of what is possible and estimates of what is the cost of the possible.

Consider first the nature of human intellect as we understand it after a half century of investigation—investigation often more orderly than startling, but yet of a nature that yields a steady knowledge. In most recent years, the quest has yielded more surprising turns as we have undertaken the job of forging compatible links between man's intellect and the computers that are its servants.

Perhaps the most pervasive feature of human intellect is its limited capacity at any moment for dealing with information. There is a rule that states that we have about seven slots, plus or minus two, through which the external world can find translation into experience. We easily become overwhelmed by complexity or clutter. Cognitive mastery in a world that generates stimuli far faster than we can sort them depends upon strategies for reducing the complexity and the clutter. But reduction must be selective, attuned to the things that "matter." Some of the modes of reduction require, seemingly, no learning—as with our adaptation mechanisms. What does not change ceases to register: steady states in their very nature cease to stimulate. Stabilize the image on the retina by getting rid of fine tremor, and the visual world fades away. There is another type of selectivity that reflects man's deepest intellectual trait and is heavily dependent on learning. Man constructs models of his world, not only templates that represent what he encounters and in what context, but also ones that permit him to be beyond them. He learns the world in a way that enables him to make predictions of what comes next by matching a few milliseconds of what is now experienced to a stored model and reading the rest from the model. We see a contour and a snatch of movement. "Ah yes, that's the night watchman checking the windows . . ." Or a patient sits before a physician complaining that vision in one eye is unaccountably dim. Both doctor and patient are involved in kindred activities. If the doctor diagnoses a scotoma, a deadened area on the retina, he does so by a process analogous to the process that leads the patient not to see a "hole" in his visual field, but a dimming, for the victim of a scotoma completes the hole by extrapolating what the rest of the eye is taking in. It is in the nature of the selectivity governed by these models that we come increasingly to register easily on those things in the world that we expect; indeed we assume that the expected is there on the basis of a minimum of information. There is compelling

16

evidence that so long as the environment conforms to the expected patterns within reasonable limits, alerting mechanisms in the brain are quietened. But once expectancy is violated, once the world ceases strikingly to correspond to our models of it (and it must be rather striking, for we ride roughshod over minor deviations), then all the alarms go off and we are at full alertness, thanks to our neural reticular system. So man can not only deal with information before him, but go far beyond the information given—with all that this implies both for swiftness of intellect and for fallibility. Almost by definition, the exercise of intellect, involving as it must the use of short cuts and of leaps from partial evidence, always courts the possibility of error. It is the good fortune of our species that not only are we also highly adept at correction (given sufficient freedom from time pressure), but have learned to institutionalize ways of keeping error within tolerable limits.

The models or stored theories of the world that are so useful in inference are strikingly generic and reflect man's ubiquitous tendency to categorize. William James remarked that the life of mind began when the child is first able to proclaim, "Aha, thingumbob again." We organize experience to represent not only the particulars that have been experienced, but the classes of events of which the particulars are exemplars. We go not only from part to whole, but irresistibly from the particular to the general. At least one distinguished linguist has argued in recent times that this generic tendency of human intellect must be innately human, for without it one could not master the complex web of categorial or substitution rules that constitutes the syntax of language—any language. Both in achieving the economy with which human thought represents the world and in effecting swift correction for error, the categorizing tendency of intelligence is central—for it yields a structure of thought that becomes hierarchically organized with growth, forming branching structures in which it is relatively easy to search for alternatives. The blunders occur, of course, where things that must be together for action or for understanding happen to be organized in different hierarchies. It is a form of error that is as familiar in science as in everyday life.

I do not mean to imply, of course, that man structures his knowledge of the world only by the categorial rules of inclusion, exclusion, and overlap, for clearly he traffics in far greater complexity, too. Witness the almost irresistible urge to see cause and effect. Rather, the categorial nature of thought underlines its rule-bound nature. The eighteenth-century assumption that knowledge grows by a gradual accretion of associations built up by contact with events that are contiguous in time, space, or quality does not fit the facts of mental life. There are spheres where such associative laws operate within limits, as for example with material that is strange and meaningless (the psychologist's nonsense syllables, for example), but for the most part organization is a far more active process of imposing order as by forming a hypothesis and then checking it to be sure.

In the main, we do the greater part of our work by manipulating our representations or models of reality rather than by acting directly on the world itself. Thought is then vicarious action, in which the high cost of error is strikingly reduced. It is characteristic of human beings and no other species that we can carry out this vicarious action with the aid of a large number of intellectual prosthetic devices that are, so to speak, tools provided by the culture. Natural language is the prime example, but there are pictorial and diagrammatic conventions as well, theories, myths, modes of reckoning and ordering. We are even able to employ devices to fulfill functions not given man through evolution, devices that bring phenomena into the human range of registering and computing: phenomena too slow to follow or too fast, too small or too large, too numerous or too few. Today, indeed we develop devices to determine whether the events we watch conform to or deviate from expectancy in comprehensible ways. My colleague George Miller put it well, speaking about computers in his Granada Lecture in 1965: "Mechanical intelligence will not ultimately replace human intelligence, but rather, by complementing our human intelligence, will supplement and amplify it. We will learn to supply by mechanical organs those functions that natural evolution has failed to provide."[1]

The range of man's intellect, given its power to be increased from the outside in, can never be estimated without considering the means a culture provides for empowering mind. Man's intellect then is not simply his own, but is communal in the sense that its unlocking or empowering depends upon the success of the culture in developing means to that end. There is a sense in which, as Professor Lévi-Strauss has taught us, human intellect does not vary in power as a function of the means and technology available to it. For the use of amplifiers of mind requires, admittedly, a commonly shared human capacity, and each society fashions and perfects this capacity to its needs. But there is, I believe, a respect in which a lack of means for understanding one matter places out of reach other matters that are crucial to man's condition whatever his culture.

Let me add one final point before turning to the evolution of primate intelligence. Human beings have three different systems, partially translatable one into the other, for representing reality. One is through action. We know some things by knowing how to do them: to ride bicycles, tie knots, swim, and so on. A second way of knowing is through imagery and those products of mind that, in effect, stop the action and summarize it in a representing ikon. While Napoleon could say that a general who thinks in images is not fit to command, it is still true that a thousand words scarcely exhaust the richness of a single image. Finally, there is representation by symbol, of which the type-case is language with its rules for forming sentences not only about what exists in experience but, by its powerful combinatorial techniques, for forming equally good ones about what might or might not exist. Each of these modes has its own skills, its own prosthetic aids, its own virtues and defects, and we shall encounter them again before we are done.

The evolution of primate intelligence is only now beginning to be understood. The evidence today is that the full evolution of human intelligence required for its movement the presence of bipedalism and tool use in early hominids. It is subsequent to these developments that we find a sharp increase in man's cranial capacity and in the size of his cerebral cortex. But the logic of the situation and indirect evidence argues that the development of tool using itself required some prior capacity, however minimal. I have recently observed a film shot in a natural park in East Africa in which a chimpanzee is using a straw, properly wetted in spittle, to insert into a termite hill to extract these insects. A baboon is watching. When his turn comes he tears the termite hill apart. Tool using of the kind found in early hominids is quite plainly a program in which tools are substituted for manual operations in much the same way that the carpenter can substitute a chisel for his forgotten plane, or a knife or even a saw blade. The evidence indicates that the change in tools used in East Africa after the first stabilization of a chopping tool was not very rapid. What was probably more important was the range of programs or activities into which this tool was substituted.

But having said that much, it is well to note that it was not a large-brained hominid that developed the technical-social way of life of the human, but rather the tool-using, cooperative pattern that gradually changed man's morphology by favoring the tool user over the heavy-jawed, smaller brained creature who depended upon his morphology alone. I have commented in passing upon the emergence of tools made to pattern, in contrast to spontaneous tools. It is at this point in human evolution, place it at some multiple of 10^5 years ago, that man comes to depend upon a culture and its technical pool in order to be able to fill his ecological niche. The biologist Peter Medawar comments in a recent Huxley Lecture that it is at about this point that human evolution becomes sufficiently elaborated to merit being called Lamarckian and reversible, rather than Darwinian and irreversible. For what is now being transmitted, over and beyond the human gene pool, is a set of acquired characteristics passed on in the cultural pool of a people. The reversibility, of course, is attested to by many splendid ruins, ruins manned by descendants with genes indistinguishable from their ancestors.

It is folly to speculate about the birth date of language. It seems likely, however, that the capacity that made possible the development of human language, the abstractive, rule-producing gift, must also have had something to do with the programmatic nature of tool using with its rules of substitution. It is not plain how we shall ever be able to reconstruct the matter.

One further feature of the evolution of intelligence relates to impulse control. We have had, in the past decade, several impressive overviews of the evolution of mammalian sexuality, from the familiar laboratory rat, through the ubiquitous macaque monkey, through the great apes, to man. The picture that emerges in the transition from lower mammals through primates is one of decreasing control by the hormonal system and an increasing part played by early experience through intervention of the cerebral cortex. Even before the emergence of higher apes, hominids, and early man, there was a striking increase in control of sexual activity by the central nervous system. With man and his ability to symbolize, the role of the central nervous system is further increased. For what is most striking in the change in sexuality from higher primates to humans is the emergence of what anthropologists speak of as classificatory kinship. In place of the sexual dominance and restricting territoriality of the higher apes, the human species seems early to have developed a pattern involving reciprocal exchange of women outward to neighboring groups, an exchange used in the formation of mutual alliances. The role of this more stable and reciprocal kinship pattern in the upbringing of young must now concern us.

Human beings have a more prolonged and dependent childhood than other primates. Present opinion concerning the origin of this condition is somewhat as follows. As hominids became increasingly bipedal, with the free hands necessary for tool using, there was not only an increase in the size of the brain, but also a requirement of a stronger pelvic girdle to withstand the impacting strain of upright walking. The increased strength of the pelvic girdle came through a gradual closing down of the birth canal, and an obstetrical paradox was produced: a larger brain, but a smaller birth canal for the neonate to pass through. The resolution seems to have been achieved through the cerebral immaturity of the human infant, not only permitting the newborn to pass through the reduced canal, but assuring a prolonged childhood during which the ways and skills of the culture could be transmitted. There are reasonable arguments to be advanced in favor of the view that the direction of evolution in the nervous system of primates from the lowly tree shrews through lemurs and tarsiers and monkeys on to the higher apes and man has been in the direction not only of more cerebral cortex and more tissue for the distance receptors, but also toward the evolutionary selection of immature forms. This tendency to neoteny, as it is called, is particularly notable in man, to the extent that the human brain more closely resembles the fetal brain of the gorilla in some respects than the adult brain of that great ape. And so, to take one index, the human brain is about

21

a quarter of adult size at birth; in rhesus monkeys and gibbons, the job is about finished after six months. And so it is argued that human infancy with its more malleable dependency can be viewed as a prolongation of the fetal period of the earlier primates.

It is not simply the length and dependency of childhood that increases in man, but also the mode of raising young to the requirements of communal life. Let me describe very briefly some salient differences in the free learning patterns of immature baboons and the children of a hunting–gathering group in a roughly comparable ecology (the !Kung Bushmen). Baboons have a highly developed social life in their troops, with well-organized and stable dominance patterns. They live within a territory, protecting themselves from predators by joint action of the strongly built, adult males. It is striking that the behavior of baboon juveniles is shaped principally by play with their peer group, play that provides opportunity for the spontaneous expression and practice of the component acts that, in maturity, will be orchestrated into the behavior either of the dominant male or of the infant-protective female. All this seems to be accomplished with little participation by any mature animals in the play of the juveniles. We know from a variety of experiments how devastating a disruption in development can be produced in subhuman primates raised in a laboratory by interfering with their opportunity for peer-group play and social interaction.

Among hunting–gathering humans, on the other hand, there is *constant* interaction between adult and child, or adult and adolescent, or adolescent and child. !Kung adults and children play and dance together, sit together, participate in minor hunting together, join in song and story telling together. At very frequent intervals, moreover, children are party to rituals presided over by adults—minor, as in the first haircutting, or major, as when a boy kills his first kudu buck and goes through the proud but painful process of scarification. Children, besides, are constantly playing imitatively with the rituals, implements, tools, and weapons of the adult world. Young juvenile baboons, on the other hand, virtually never play with things or imitate directly large and significant sequences of adult behavior.

Note, however, that among the !Kung one virtually never sees an instance of "teaching" taking place outside the situation where the behavior to be learned is relevant. Nobody "teaches" in our prepared sense of the word. There is nothing like school, nothing like lessons. Indeed, among the !Kung there is very little "telling." Most of what we would call instruction is through showing. In the end, everybody in the culture knows nearly all there is to know about how to get on with life as a man or as a woman.

The change in the instruction of children in more complex societies is twofold. First of all, there is knowledge and skill in the culture far in excess of what any one individual knows. And so increasingly there develops an economical technique of instructing the young based heavily on *telling* out of context rather than *showing* in context. The result of "teaching the culture" can, at its worst, lead to the ritual, rote nonsense that has led generations of critics to despair. But school imposes indirect demands that may be one of the most important departures from indigenous practice. It takes learning, as we have noted, out of the context of immediate action just by dint of putting it into a school. This very extirpation makes learning become an act in itself, freed from the immediate ends of action, preparing the learner for that form of reckoning that is remote from payoff and conducive to reflectiveness. In school, moreover, one must "follow the lesson," which means one must learn to follow either the abstraction of written speech—abstract in the sense that it is divorced from the concrete situation to which the speech might originally have been related—or the abstraction of language delivered orally but out of the context of an on-going action. Both of these are highly abstract uses of language.

It is no wonder, then, that many recent studies report large differences between "primitive" children who are in schools and their brothers who are not: differences in perception, abstraction, time perspective, and so on.

Let me now describe very briefly some of the major aspects of intellectual growth as we observe it in the growing child. The first and most general thing that can be said is that it does not flow smoothly, but rather in spurts of rapid growth followed by consolidation. The spurts in growth seem to be organized around the emergence of certain capacities, including intellectual capacities. These latter have about them the character of prerequisites: one thing must be mastered before the child can go on to the next. Many of them are directed to two ends: the maintenance of invariance and the transcending of momentaneousness in registration and response. Let me say a word about each.

By invariance, we mean the recognition of kinship and continuity in things that are transformed either in location or appearance or in the response they evoke. The child must first learn to distinguish that objects have a persistent identity beyond the identity endowed upon them by the action one takes toward them. He then learns that an object persists beyond one's visual or tactile contact with it so that out of sight is not out of mind and a new appearance is not a new thing. He must then travel the long road of decentration, as Piaget (who has taught us so much about mental development) calls it: being able to represent things not only from the egocentric axis, but from other vantage points, personally as well as geometrically. In time, the child moves (at least in our culture) from a representation of the world through action to a representation based very heavily upon the appearance of things. Water poured from a standard beaker into one that is longer and thinner is now said by the four-year-old to be more water because it is "taller than before." In time, the child recognizes that there is constancy across change in appearance. What he is doing in the process of mastering invariance is, of course, constructing increasingly stable models of the world, increasingly comprehensive ones capable of reducing the surface complexity of the world to the limits of his capacity for dealing with information. In good season, and always with help from the culture, the child develops models or modes of representation that are far more symbolic or linguistic in nature. The growth of invariance, then, takes place with the development of the enactive, ikonic, and symbolic representations we examined earlier. Students of the developmental process agree in broad outline about this progress, though the details and the terminology differ as one travels west from Moscow to Geneva to Paris to Cambridge to Denver to Berkeley.

With respect to transcending momentaneousness, let me illustrate by citing a child, age five, who said of the larger of two half-filled beakers that it was fuller than the other, a moment later that it was also emptier, and then a moment later in answer to a question that it could not be both fuller and emptier. He worked with a consistent logic and saw no contradiction. The logic was self-sufficient for each episode and the three in question were not put together to make possible the recognition of contradiction. The bigger glass was fuller because it appeared to have more water; the bigger was also emptier because it appeared to have more empty space; a vessel could not be both emptier and fuller because, to cite the product of the child's *Sprachgefühl,* "that's silly." Again, development provides models that permit the child to sense coherence over larger and larger segments of experience, time- and space-binding representations that permit wider ranges of connection.

Save in the artificial setting of the school, dominated as it is by telling and a lack of guiding feedback, there is an extraordinary property of self-reward about the act of learning during growth. The satisfaction of curiosity seems to be self-rewarding among all primates. So, too, the development of competence. More uniquely human, finally, is that mysterious process whereby human beings pattern themselves on another and gain satisfaction by maintaining the supposed standard of their model. The three self-rewarding processes provide a motor for growth that is stalled only by repeated failure or by an inability to determine how one is progressing at a task. This does not mean, of course, that what a child learns is what is most empowering of his capacities but, rather, what happens to be available. It is here that the innovation of school and teacher can be critically important.

Consider now the nature of codified knowledge as it might affect our views about the perfectibility of intellect. The past half century has surely been one of the richest as well as the most baffling in the history of our effort to understand the nature of knowledge. Advances in the foundation of mathematics and logic, in the philosophy of science, in the theory of information processing, in linguistics, and in psychology—all of these have led to new formulations and new conjectures.

Perhaps the greatest change, stemming principally from the revolutions in physics, is in our conception of what a theory is. For Newton, inquiry was a voyage on the sea of ignorance to find the islands of truth. We know now that theory is more than a general description of what happens or a statement of probabilities of what might or might not happen—even when it claims to be nothing more than that, as in some of the newer behavioral sciences. It entails, explicitly or implicitly, a model of what it is that one is theorizing about, a set of propositions that, taken in ensemble, yield occasional predictions about things. Armed with a theory, one is guided toward what one will treat as data, is predisposed to treat some data as more relevant than others. A theory is also a way of stating tersely what one already knows without the burden of detail. In this sense it is a canny and economical way of keeping in mind a vast amount while thinking about a very little.

Discussing the organization of thought, Whitehead remarks in *The Aims of Education,* "Mankind found itself in possession of certain concepts respecting nature—for example, the concept of fairly permanent material bodies—and proceeded to determine laws which related the corresponding percepts in nature. But the formulation of laws changed the concepts, sometimes gently by an added precision, sometimes violently. At first this process was not much noticed or at least was felt to be a process curbed within narrow bounds, not touching fundamental ideas. At the stage where we now are, the formulation of the concepts can be seen to be as important as the formulation of the empirical laws connecting the events in the universe as thus conceived by us."[2] What is perhaps most important about this way of viewing theory is the attitude it creates toward the use of mind. We now see the construction of theory as a way of using the mind, the imagination, of standing off from the activities of observation and inference and creating a shape of nature.

It can also be said of knowledge that, though it is constrained by the very mode of its expression, it can be expressed in various modes. There is a continuity between knowing how to operate a seesaw, being able to describe a balance beam and cause it to balance with weights placed differentially on either side, knowing that three ounces six inches from the center of the balance will be equal to six ounces at three inches or two ounces at nine inches or eighteen ounces at one inch, and finally, knowing Newton's conception of moments. This partial isomorphism between more and less abstract ways of knowing

26

something, though it gives the appearance of great obviousness, has implications that are all too easily overlooked.

Let me comment on a point that has preoccupied Dr. Oppenheimer: the connexity of knowledge. There is an implosion of knowledge just as there is an explosion. As observations have become more numerous, the ways in which they may be integrated and connected by powerful theories have also increased. Where the danger lies, of course, is in the possibility that fewer men will come to know the larger and more comprehensive domains to which such theories can be related. But there is reason to question such an eventuality. For it may be that the technologies now being devised for storing, relating, and retrieving information may change the very texture of the intellectual community. Crude though its present conception may be, the idea of a society of scholars connected to a data base through computational devices and programs that can quickly retrieve related information, suggests that we may have automatic servants and assistants vital to the pursuit of connection. We can begin to envisage ways of making knowledge less inert and discrete than it is now, when placed on the shelves of libraries or within the pages of our journals. What is required is a means of constantly rearranging and reordering knowledge in a fashion to reflect the theoretical advances and hypotheses current in the intellectual community that uses the knowledge.

The disciplines of learning represent not only codified knowledge but ways of thought, habits of mind, implicit assumptions, short cuts, and styles of humor that never achieve explicit statement. Concentrations of these ways of thought probably account for the phenomenal productivity in ideas and men of, say, the Cavendish Laboratory under Rutherford or Copenhagen under Bohr. For these ways of thought keep knowledge lively, keep the knower sensitive to opportunity and anomaly. I draw attention to this matter, for studies in the history of knowledge suggest that deadening and banalization are also characteristics of knowledge once it becomes codified.

I apologize for this headlong dash through the domain of cognition and, indeed, beg your forbearance for the major omissions, particularly one. I have concentrated on right-handed knowledge and given short shrift to the left hand—to the disciplines of art, of poetry, of history, of drama, and of metaphysics. Several implications follow from the account that I have given that bear not only upon the perfectibility of man's intellect, but also upon the process of its perfecting. Let me in conclusion, then, comment upon a few of these.

In speaking of the nature of intellectual functioning, its evolution, its growth, and its codified products, I have placed heavy emphasis upon the role of models or theories that human beings build to render the varieties of experience into some manageable and economical form. Man creates theories before he creates tools. His capacity and skill for catching the invariances of the world around him probably underlie not only his success as a tool user and tool maker, but also his use of that powerful instrument for expression and thought, human language. His myths, his art, his ritual, his sciences are all expressions of this deep-lying tendency to explicate and condense, to seek steady meaning in capricious experience.

Many scholars in this country and abroad have been involved this past decade in what has come popularly to be called the "curriculum revolution," the effort to start children younger and more effectively on the way to grasping the more powerful ideas embodied in the learned disciplines. And indeed it is a revolution in at least one obvious respect: the union of men at the frontiers of knowledge with those charged with instructing the young, the two working jointly on the conversion of learning into a form comprehensible and nutritious to the young. The effort is also recentering the work of psychologists and others concerned with the development of children, though we are only beginning to understand the means whereby intellectual development can be assisted. It is in this activity that I see a fresh approach to the perfectibility of intellect. Let me explain.

Once granted that a principal task of intellect is in the construction of explanatory models for the ordering of experience, the immediate problem then becomes one of converting the most powerful ways of knowing into a form that is within the grasp of a young learner. Let curriculum consist of a series of prerequisites in knowledge and in skill, to be mastered with an in-built reward in increased competence as the learner goes from one step to the next. Such a view assumes that for any knowledge or empowering skill that exists in the culture there is a corresponding form that is within the grasp of a young learner at the stage of development where one finds him—that any subject can be taught to anybody at any age in some form that is both interesting and honest. Once mastered in that appropriate form, the learner can go on to more powerful, more precise forms of knowing and of using knowledge. It is already reasonably clear that this can be done in mathematics and science—though we are very, very far from doing it well. But it is also the case that reading simpler poetry brings more complex poetry into reach, or that reading a poem once makes a second reading more rewarding.

The conception of a curriculum as an effort to go more deeply and more powerfully and more precisely into a body of knowledge before one risks traveling more widely carries with it a self-limiting but benign constraint. One must choose the subjects one teaches from domains of knowledge robust and deep enough to permit such revisits. But it is not so much the subject matter that is at issue. The more "elementary" a course and the younger its pupils, the more serious must be its pedagogical aim of forming the intellectual powers of those whom it serves. It is as important to justify a good mathematics course by the intellectual discipline it provides or the honesty it promotes as by the mathematics it transmits. It cannot do one without the other.

Invention is required if one is to proceed in this way. How convert knowledge into the form that is within the grasp of a learner, so that he may be tempted on? Recall the three modes of knowing characteristic of human cognitive operations—by action, by image, and by symbol. One approach to the task that has proved moderately successful is to begin a sequence of learning with an enactive representation—learning inertial physics by operating levers, learning music by composing and playing in a highly simplified musical notation, and so on. One goes beyond that to intuitive, image-laden forms, as with intuitive geometry or the kind of visual aids by which formal logic can be rendered in Venn diagrams, and finally to the increasingly abstract symbolic modes of a field of learning.

A more difficult task is to instill early in the learner what in effect is a balance between impatience with the trivial as proof against clutter and an open spirit toward what might be but is not obviously relevant. Here again, the experience of those who have worked on constructing

29

curriculum suggests that one plunge right in. Short of that, it is difficult to accomplish anything. One starts concretely trying to give some feeling for the way of thought that is a discipline and one often succeeds. Again, it is as with musical instruction where one gives the learner the simplest possible Mozart rather than a scale so that as early as possible he may sense what music is.

Above all, what emerges from the past decade of experimenting with instruction is the importance of increasing the child's power of thought by inventing for him modes of access to the empowering techniques of the culture. The nature of a school as an instrument for doing this is very unclear. The perfecting of intellect begins earlier than we thought and goes communally from the outside in as well as growing from within. Perhaps the task of converting knowledge into a form fit for this function is, after all, the final step in our codification of knowledge. Perhaps the task is to go beyond the learned scholarship, scientific research, and the exercise of disciplined sensibility in the arts to the transmission of what we have discovered. Surely no culture will reach its full potential unless it invents ever better means for doing so.

REFERENCES

1. MILLER, GEORGE A., Computers, communication, and cognition. *Advancement of Science,* vol. 21, no. 93, pp. 417–430, Jan. 1965.
2. WHITEHEAD, ALFRED NORTH, The aims of education and other essays, 247 pp. New York: Macmillan, 1929.

HERBERT BUTTERFIELD

Herbert Butterfield was born in 1900, the son of Albert Butterfield and Ada Mary Buckland. He received his education at Keighley Trade and Grammar School in Yorkshire, and later was a scholar at Peterhouse, Cambridge.

A fellow of Peterhouse from 1923 to 1955, Professor Butterfield has served as Master there since 1955. Starting in 1944 as a professor of modern history at Cambridge University, he was made Regius Professor in 1963. He has also been a Jane Eliza Procter Visiting-Fellow at Princeton University (1924–25); lecturer in history, Peterhouse, Cambridge (1930–44); editor, *Cambridge Historical Journal* (1938–52); president, Historical Association (1955–58); member of the executive board, International Association of Universities, since 1960; and Vice-Chancellor, University of Cambridge (1959–61).

He wrote his first book, *The Historical Novel*, which was awarded the Le Bas Prize at Cambridge, in 1924. At the same time he was being trained in diplomatic history by Harold Temperley. From these studies evolved his *The Peace Tactics of Napoleon, 1806–8* (1929), which led him to write his brief life of Napoleon for Duckworth & Company's Great Lives series (1939). In 1931 appeared *The Whig Interpretation of History,* which provoked considerable controversy. In the following years he turned his attention to the Renaissance and produced *The Statecraft of Machiavelli* (1940). In 1947 he was appointed chairman of Cambridge's committee for the establishment of the teaching of the history of science and delivered on this topic a series of lectures published in 1949 under the title *The Origins of Modern Science, 1300–1800.*

In the meantime he had begun to work on the history of historical scholarship, and in this connection he wrote *The Englishman and His History* (1944) and *Man on His Past* (1955), as well as some essays on historical method and some studies of Lord Acton. He has been interested in the relations between history and various aspects of life, and this has led him to produce *Christianity*

31

and History (1949), *Christianity, Diplomacy and War* (1953), and *International Conflict in the Twentieth Century* (1960). He was Riddell Lecturer at the University of Durham in 1951 and Wiles Trust Lecturer at the University of Belfast in 1954, and he is delivering the Gifford Lectures at the University of Glasgow, 1965–66.

He is planning to write a life of Charles James Fox, and in connection with his studies in this field he published, in 1949, *George III, Lord North and the People,* and, in 1957, *George III and the Historians.*

History as the Organization of
Man's Memory

HERBERT BUTTERFIELD

WE OFTEN THINK of Western civilization as scientific, and we do not always remember that it is equally remarkable for being so historically-minded. In both respects the only parallel to it is ancient China—so wonderful in its science and technology, but possessing also a historical literature of almost incredible vastness. Even in China there did not develop those modern techniques which, in our section of the globe, led to the scientific revolution of the seventeenth century and the somewhat parallel historiographical revolution in the nineteenth. In both fields the developments in Europe were unique; and the Chinese have had to become the pupils of the West.

Some civilizations, like that of ancient India, seem to have been governed by religions or philosophies which deny significance to the facts of history as such, and the sequence of events in time. Yet, between a culture that has soaked itself in historical memories and one for which the past is only chance and change—only froth and foam—there must develop great differences in general mentality, in intellectual habits, and in the degree of control that can be acquired over the course of events. And the differences must extend to still deeper things that affect the very nature of the human consciousness.

Our interest in the past—our very sense for the past (like our prowess in the natural sciences)—is therefore a thing that requires to be explained. Even the case that we today might make for the study of history would have no meaning for those earlier generations of mankind that gave the start to the whole endeavor. We of the twentieth century might say that a society is going to be very constricted in its development unless it looks behind itself, organizes its memory, reflects on its larger and longer experiences, learns to measure the direction in which it is moving, and gets some notion of long-term tendencies that have been observed. But this kind of diagnosis—this way of learning where we stand in the processes of time—is a thing that comes only late in the day, when civilization and scholarship itself have progressed very far. Nobody could have known in advance that by the study of the past we should be able to examine the processes of things in time. Indeed, until the world was fairly mature, nobody could even have guessed that there existed such things as historical processes which might call for analysis.

It is possible that, in every age and society, children will love to listen to the tales of a grandfather and will look back at least to the time just before they were born. All the world seems to love a story, and, even if there were no inferences to be drawn from it, we are all likely to be interested in the account by Arthur M. Schlesinger, Jr., of the expedition to the Bay of Pigs—interested in it purely as the narrative of something that actually happened. I suspect that, however scientific and analytical and statistical historical scholarship may become in the latter half of the twentieth century, a great mass of people will go on loving this narrative history—the history that tells of men and their vicissitudes. And perhaps these are the people who will keep the subject sane—keep history an important humanistic factor in our civilization. But, though the telling of stories may awaken an interest in the past, it is not likely in itself to alter the structure of our mentality. Also it is hardly enough in itself to drive the mind to research and criticism and the passionate quest for truth. The raconteur knows that if he investigates the truth of the matter he is only too likely to lose a good story.

Before writing began, the past would seem to have been just a ragbag of old myths and stories—a jumble of things that happened "once upon a time." An essential progress was achieved when the mind learned to project itself into that forest of data and began to acquire some sense of the distances involved. It was necessary that time should be turned into something like a long tape measure, with markings that roughly indicated succession and duration and degrees of remoteness. This is not easily achieved by peoples who have not learned to serialize or particularize the years by numbering them in the way that we are accustomed to doing. Fortunately, our distant ancestors appear to have had a mania for making lists. Some of these lists are in a sense the beginning of history, just as others—which perform a preliminary work of classification—are in a sense the beginning of the natural sciences. It was when they put together their lists of successive kings or priests that these ancient peoples acquired their first impressions of the tremendous stretch of time behind them. The ancient Greeks had very defective lists and thought that only a comparatively short period separated them from the age when the gods had walked and sported on the earth. But some of them learned about the colossal lists of Egyptian priests and came to realize that there had been thousands of years of human history before their day. If the whole of this is taken together, it involves a change in what might be called the human consciousness, a deeper sense of what it means to have an existence in time—in a time that stretches behind and before.

It is comparatively easy for an individual to keep some recollection of his own personal past; but the difficulties are great if the human race or the body politic wants to achieve and organize and refine its collective memory. In the civilization of ancient Mesopotamia the arts had reached a remarkable level and technology had done wonderful things before there existed any serious history. Even in the modern centuries the development of historical scholarship has proceeded at a slower pace than that of the natural sciences; and the intellectual revolution—with the modern techniques of discovery—comes in this field only with the nineteenth (rather than the seventeenth) century. In generations that were capable of the most profound philosophy and the most abstruse mathematics there would flourish a remarkable credulity about the records and stories of the past. In the middle of the nineteenth century, when the archives of the European capitals were being opened, a great stimulus was given to the subject—men felt that now, at last, they could really get down to the study of history. For centuries before that they had more or less accepted the history provided for them, but it is not clear that they committed their souls to it, save where it was guaranteed by revealed religion. The truth is that men did not realize how many of the facts of history were going to be capable of more secure establishment in the future.

So it seems that Homer was accepted as history at first—the only available account—though the Greeks had not yet scrutinized very carefully their notion of historicity. For the knowledge of these early periods it was perhaps a handicap that in Homer they possessed such an impressive substitute for history. The epics were so regarded as the genuine article that the first serious attempts at historical criticism were directed at their contents. There was no possibility of discovering dates, but family trees were important, and some of the Greek noble families claimed descent from epic heroes. Here, legend and history seem to meet. It would appear to be genealogy that first called for investigation.

The remoter period always presented special difficulties. It was no easy matter to recover recollections that had once been lost. A short-term memory was a more practicable affair, however; and the more serious kind of history developed through the recording of recent events. It is possible that in every age and society men refer to the past—if only to the recent past—for the understanding of present-day problems and even for their very formulation. Because we ourselves have become so historically-minded, and because we have come to be so aware of the continuity of processes in history, we carry this tendency almost infinitely further than our distant forefathers took it. Whether we are discussing Vietnam or the incidence of prostitution, we slip into a kind of historical retrospect before we are aware of what we are doing. With us at least, it seems that talk about the present slides almost insensibly into talk about the past. But even thousands of years ago—and even before the existence of historical study—the same tendency is visible on occasion and it operated as a stimulus to historiography. One of the earliest pieces of historical narrative that we possess is a royal account of a quarrel over a frontier. The victor in the conflict, as he announced its settlement and laid out the case, referred back to the original fixing of the boundary and the successive infringements of it by his enemy. Some of the most remarkable examples of historical writing in the ancient world come from the

Hittites who, centuries before any part of the Old Testament had been written, provided their peace treaties with historical preambles, and would even produce a similar résumé to explain an act of governmental policy. The very considerable historical literature of ancient Egypt and Assyria was the work of people who showed no sign of having any real interest in the past. It came from monarchs who desired to place on record their own building achievements, their prowess in the hunt, and their victories in battle. What they intended was either to overawe their contemporaries or to make sure of their future fame or to express their gratitude to the gods. There developed, therefore, the history of the type of the commemorative tablet, and it was produced on a massive scale, sometimes with elaborate literary ornament, but it was bound to lead to a dead end. At the same time it remained true for thousands of years, that the history which most gripped the rails and came closest to authenticity was that which men wrote about the events in which they had taken part or which they had more or less observed. The attempt to reconstruct a distant past from raw materials—from literary and archeological survivals—is on the whole a remarkably modern enterprise. The best history was like that of Thucydides—like that of Winston Churchill—giving his account of the great wars in which he had taken part.

The Old Testament brought things to a new stage. It envisaged the whole of mankind from the Creation and then presented a full-length national history. The influence of its presiding idea helped to give shape to what became the Western view of the time process.

The ancient Hebrews had been a semi-nomadic people, and it was characteristic of such clans that they yearned to enter the territory of the sedentary populations and share the benefits of settled agricultural life. They expected their god to vindicate himself by procuring this; and the most vivid of the Hebrew folk-memories concerned the way in which they had been brought out of the land of Egypt to the country of the Promise. By all the rules of the game they ought to have then proceeded to adopt the nature gods and the fertility rites of settled agricultural peoples; but their semi-nomadic beliefs prevailed, and they turned from the gods of nature to the God of history. When others had ceremonies for the cycle of the seasons, they preferred to celebrate historical events. If young people asked why they should obey the commandments, the answer was: "Because God brought us up out of the land of Egypt." They stressed the fact that their God had kept his Promise, and this Promise was a developing thing, always turning out to be something higher than had previously been thought. Also their nation was to be blessed by heaven at the finish. History pointed to a grand consummation sometime in the future.

History, then, was not merely cyclic—mere aimless revolving and vain repetition. The ancient Hebrews would insist on occasion that God, besides being the original Creator, could go on doing new things as time proceeded. Christianity itself emerged as a "historical" religion in a peculiarly technical sense of the word. We can see the way in which St. Augustine decided that the cyclic view of history was incompatible with Christianity. The West developed under the presidency of these Jewish ideas and for over fifteen hundred years the men of Europe could learn about their religion only through a Bible that was packed with history.

Later ages have seen in the Old Testament almost an adumbration of the future idea of progress. Toward the end of the seventeenth and in the eighteenth century this idea was superseding cyclic views and the belief that the natural processes of time bring decadence—superseding notions taken over from the ancient world. The change was partly due to the realization of the accumulating achievements of the sciences and technology. But the general idea of progress may have involved an element of faith—a belief in the future, almost the notion of history as based on the Promise. Once the idea of progress had emerged it gave a further stimulus to the study of history itself. Now it was possible to organize the memory a little more, to give shape to the human story, and to see the whole in terms of development. It was possible to put to history a further range of questions. One could ask it to show how mankind, from its primitive beginnings, had come to its present civilized state.

There was a sense in which men had always gone to history for answers to questions; and almost before they had any history they would investigate genealogies, as we have seen. At the next stage, certain miscellaneous problems tended to attract them. We meet these in ancient Mesopotamia, in the Old Testament, among the ancient Greeks, in Renaissance Europe, and elsewhere. Once the initial curiosity was aroused, the same type of question seems to have been presented everywhere. People wanted to know why mankind had been divided into nations and why, among the nations, there was such a confusion of tongues. They asked how tribes and cities and rivers had got their names. They wondered why a certain place—a well or a mountain perhaps—had come to be considered sacred. At this stage of their development, the question would be answered by the telling of a story. In ancient Babylonia the priests rather than the monarchs were responsible for the records, and they tended to bring history closer to the problems of human destiny. Here was particularly observed the device of explaining things by giving an account of their origins—in other words, producing a myth.

It was in ancient Greece that questions began to be answered more effectively; and the advance was connected with a wider rationalizing movement, a great development in what we should call the sciences. It was assisted by the fact that an interest in neighboring countries had led to geographical and ethnographical studies; and history emerged in Greece as almost the byproduct of these. It made its appearance in a more scientific context; and there was a disposition to account for both geographical and historical phenomena on more naturalistic lines. The belief that the gods constantly interfered in the course of events must hitherto have obstructed the discovery of laws and processes in history.

The leadership of the Greeks became most important, however, in the scientific use of the facts that the historian establishes; and this came to Europe at the Renaissance. They learned to extract from all the complexity of material certain types of data that could be usefully collated with one another. A famous example of this was followed by Machiavelli when he set out to show that politics should be handled in a scientific manner. He produced a comparative study of all the conspiracies of history from which it was possible, for example, to discover maxims for men who wanted to assassinate their king. Perhaps the most famous and successful use of this method is the case of the Marxists studying all the revolutions of history for the purpose of arriving at a proper technique of revolution.

But the more scientific treatment which the Greeks tried to give to established historical data—the hunt for correspondences and correlations—led in the long run to a different way of thinking and talking about man's activity in the world, a different sense of the part that he plays in the unrolling of time. It brought into existence the consciousness of the processes that take place in the course of human history. For the political analyst the city states of Greece were excellent laboratory specimens, where the processes (the transition from monarchy to democracy, for example) took place on a comparatively small scale—not too complicated by other things, fairly visible to the naked eye, and telescoped into a reasonably short period of time. The processes could be examined, and, for example, it was not the modern Marxists but the world of classical antiquity that first brought out the significance of the class conflict in the whole development of things. The coming of the modern idea of progress greatly increased the disposition to look for deeper movements underlying the whole human drama. Whereas history had once been written as though it involved mere acts of will on the part of men and gods—acts of will taking place in the free air—there emerged the view that human beings are involved in processes, entangled in systems of conditioning circumstance. Whereas one's first impulse is to blame entirely the wills of a few people for the outbreak of the war of 1914, Professor Temperley pointed out that one must go back at least as far as Bismarck in 1871 for the origin of that war. Over the course of the centuries the actual writing of history has changed its character; therefore, its texture is no longer that of the mere story—the story of men doing just this and then that. What we call historical narrative in a man like Ranke or even Macaulay has a more analytical quality— the story wrapped up in expositions of processes and conditioning circumstance.

Furthermore, from the quasiscientific use of the kind of data that the historian establishes there sprang a sort of political science, but later also political economy, various types of social study, and other specializations like military strategy. They became autonomous and separated themselves from history; and in the course of time some of them were able to emerge as rivals to it. They have occasionally tried to make the return journey—their results are fed back into history and they may end by trying to secure dominion over it. We may be told that, in the last analysis, it is the study of the economic substructure of history that really matters. In the twentieth century—and not least in the United States—the relations between history and the social sciences have formed a crucial issue, for some have wanted to see history interpreted as really a branch of social science. On the other hand, the question might arise as to whether, after all the associated kinds of science have been abstracted from it, there is anything left for the residual study—mere history.

We can see, therefore, how the memory of the human race has tended to acquire a certain form and organization. In general, the study of the past has affected at different levels our consciousness of life in time and our feeling for the processes of time. It alters our vision of the present day, just as a piece of landscape must look different when the observer has the eye of a geologist. It affects our everyday habits of mind; and somebody has said that in the nineteenth century all thought ran to history, a fact very noticeable in politics, theology, philosophy, and even natural science. Between this last and the study of history there have been interesting interactions, particularly at the birth of rationalism in early Greece and after the scientific revolution of the seventeenth century. From the eighteenth century even the scientists were showing a consciousness of time, as though the ultimate objective was to lay out the whole story of the physical universe. It should be remembered that, though we think of the historian as recovering the truth about the past, he is often revealing things never previously known to any man. We no longer hold the view (which until comparatively recently was sufficient for our predecessors) that somebody in the past always knew the truth about what had happened, and all that is necessary is to find this man. In the crisis of July, 1914, every foreign office in Europe would have internal knowledge of only its own policy and its own reactions to the conduct of other powers. The historian, using the papers of all the foreign offices concerned, can reach a kind of knowledge not possessed by any of the statesmen of the time. He can therefore give a higher organization to the whole story.

It is proper, moreover, that history should hold its ground as a thing possessing its own function and nature. Those who try to show from psychoanalysis what "must" have happened may be liable to contra-

diction by new documentary evidence. Events are not always historically established if the case in their favor depends on some economic
theory that is fashionable at the moment. There is need for a form of
study that in a sense keeps close to earth, merely establishing what it
was that actually "happened." The need is all the greater, and the
point becomes fundamental, if we remember how much, in the workings of time, must still depend on the wills of human beings. We
cannot exempt the men of July, 1914, from all responsibility or
pretend that everything was predetermined, the present simply the
direct product of the past. Between the past and the future there
always lie the decisions that human beings make in the living present.
Because these can never be simply inferred, we must go to the
evidence for them, and history must remain an empirical study. Men
may be entangled in a network of conditioning circumstance, but it is
live men who are so entangled—men liable to make one decision at
breakfast-time and a different one at dinner-time. It is important not
to lose sight of these live human beings and not to eliminate their role
by saying that they are mere products of their age. They are individual
fountains of life and action, and all the factors that play upon their
minds are churned and recombined inside each of them, so that we
can still never quite predict their action. Sometimes the historical
processes which seem to paralyze their activity can bring a colossal
leverage to the force that a single one of them exerts. At the same
time, the view that recognizes this importance of the personality in the
machinery of time must always allow a similar force to the operation
of contingency. A short story may tell about hundreds of tiny actions,
but one single coincidence among these may transform the entire
development. Once again, we require not merely a science of general
laws but also an empirical study of detailed happenings and a search
for the ones that are pivotal. There is something in history to which
justice cannot be done save by the kind of narrative in which we do
not quite know what is going to happen next. It is true, then, that we
need to study all that system of necessity which conditions human
action, and interpretations of history tend to be commentaries on just
that system. But we examine it rather to increase our control; we learn
about it so that we may know better where our freedom lies. Because
history so involves the awareness of this play of personality, it may be
the safeguard for humanism in a technological civilization.

SIR KENNETH MACKENZIE CLARK

Sir Kenneth Clark, born in London on July 13, 1903, is a scholar of international reputation in the art of the Italian Renaissance and is much in demand as a lecturer and world authority on Leonardo da Vinci and Piero della Francesca, being frequently consulted on the authenticity of work attributed to them and other artists, and is quite involved in aiding his government in its role as a patron of the arts.

Sir Kenneth was educated at Winchester and Trinity College, Oxford. On his first visit to Italy, in 1924, he attracted the attention of Bernard Berenson who invited him to help with the revision of his *Drawings of the Florentine Painters*. He worked with Berenson from 1926 to 1928. He had already written his book on the Gothic Revival, which was published in 1929. In 1931 he was made head of the Art Museum in Oxford, and in 1934 he became the youngest man to be appointed Director of the British National Gallery, a post he held until the end of 1945. He has also served as Surveyor of the King's Pictures, member of the Ministry of Information during World War II, Slade Professor of Fine Art at Oxford, and Chairman of the Arts Council of Great Britain, of which he was a founder. He was also the first chairman of the Independent Television authority. He received his knighthood in 1938.

Sir Kenneth's years as Director of the British National Gallery were interrupted in 1939 by the war. Aside from his work with the Ministry of Information, he served as Chairman of the War Artists Advisory Committee which commissioned artists to record various aspects of the British war effort and this marked one of the country's first ventures into state art patronage. From 1953 to 1960 Clark was Chairman of the Arts Council of Great Britain. The Council is the government agency that supports opera, drama, the leading orchestras, and art exhibitions. From 1954 to 1957, as the first chairman of Britain's ITA, his task was to insure that high standards of taste would be maintained in the program content and

43

advertising of the only commercial television station in Great Britain. When he left ITA in 1957 independent television was firmly established in Britain.

Clark's earliest book was *The Gothic Revival* (1929), a survey of the Gothic movement written when he was 21 but not published then. As a scholar of Italian art, he made his name by his definitive *Catalogue of the Drawings of Leonardo da Vinci in the Collection of His Majesty the King at Windsor Castle* (1935). He later (1939) wrote a monograph on Leonardo, which has gone into several editions. His best known book is *The Nude* (1956), which is an expansion of the 1953 Mellon Lectures in the Fine Arts delivered at the National Gallery of Art in Washington, D.C.; this and *Landscape into Art* (1949), which discusses the development of landscape painting as a distinct art form, have been translated into many languages. Other writings include *Piero della Francesca* (1951), *Ruskin Today* (1964), and *Looking at Pictures* (1960), in which 16 masterpieces are analyzed. He has also published a number of speculative articles on art, including *Moments of Vision, Art and Society,* and *The Blot and the Diagram.* Recently he gave the Wrightsman Lectures at New York University on "Rembrandt and the Italian Renaissance."

Sir Kenneth has been named a fellow of the British Academy (1949) and Companion of Honour (1959). He holds the Serena Medal of the British Academy (1955) for Italian studies, and the Banister Fletcher Prize (1958). He has degrees from the universities of Glasgow and Liverpool, and Columbia, Oxford, and London universities. He is a trustee of the British Museum; an honorary member of the Royal Scottish Academy; an honorary fellow of the Royal Institute of British Architects and the Royal College of Art; Commander of the French Legion of Honor and of the Order of the Crown of Italy; and holder of the Grand Cross of Merit of Austria.

The London *Observer** has written of Sir Kenneth that it is as a "cultural advocate" that he is happiest. "He is, in fact, the nearest thing we have got to the Continental conception of a Minister of Fine Arts, influencing all our tastes."

*March 30, 1958.

The Value of Art
in an Expanding World

SIR KENNETH MACKENZIE CLARK

THOSE OF US participating in this symposium have been asked to try and estimate how things stand in our own fields of intellectual or scholarly activity. I must try to answer for the visual arts, and for the historical and critical writing that accompanies, and should, as far as possible, keep pace with creative activity. It is a less rewarding task than that which falls to the lot of the physicist, biologist, or even the astronomer. In the sciences, methods and conclusions may vary, but there is at least agreement as to the end: to measure as accurately as possible, to know as much as possible. And there is no real uncertainty about the *value* of what is being undertaken by science, either in terms of pure knowledge, or in terms of the useful mastery of our environment.

When we consider the arts the position is very different. The value set on works of art, in both material and philosophical terms, has long been open to dispute. Social philosophers from Plato to Tolstoy have tried to link it with human welfare, but their conclusions have never squared with experience. It is not accurate to maintain that art influences conduct; at most we can say that it furnishes the mind with certain symbols which may be of benefit to our moral and spiritual life. For the past hundred years or more, most people would have agreed that the value of art depends on its power to produce a kind of exalted happiness which is an end in itself. We have grown accustomed to this position, but it has disadvantages. For although no one supposes that art can be reduced to a table of measurable values—

45

that would be contrary to its whole nature—all the values by which we live should be, to some extent, defensible in human terms, and this the value of art has ceased to be.

The extraordinary thing is that, in spite of its elusive and shadowy character, art has been accepted by millions of people who have never experienced it directly. It is the most mysterious example of minority rule in the whole field of human activity.

Can this curious situation be maintained? At first sight it would seem that there has never been a time when works of art have been so highly valued. I am not thinking primarily of the vast prices which they fetch at auctions: this is an economic question involving many complex factors, scarcity, surpluses, prestige, and even the shortage of labor that prevents rich people from spending their money on large estates and yachts. I am thinking of the enormously increased attendances at museums and galleries, the sales of expensive books, and the general air of prosperity and demand that surrounds the production and distribution of art.

But turn from the active to the contemplative sphere and one finds that never has there been a time with so little confidence in absolute values. The criteria by which works of art are judged become every day more uncertain, as the works themselves become more remote from direct experience. The language of criticism grows more incomprehensible and gives the impression that the critic is hiding his own bewilderment in a succession of complicated metaphors; and historians of art, to whom we might reasonably turn for a stable set of values, have washed their hands of the whole question. They study works of art as documents, irrespective of the qualities which, in the end, make them worth studying; they examine problems of iconology which can be illustrated just as well by a bad work of art as by a good one. And, in general historical terms, they adopt a relativist position, which considers all values in art as matters of fashion.

This is a dangerous state of opinion, because it encourages cynicism and reaction. In spite of the spread of art galleries and the proliferation of art books, art is still very much the preserve of a minority, and if a sort of Luther were to arise and, in the name of common humanity, point a scornful finger at the paraphernalia of art, conspicuous waste, as Veblen called it, he might well bring down the whole elaborate structure, unless the believers in art could produce a rather more solid body of doctrine than they seem able to do at present.

It is significant that in considering the present uneasy state of art one should invoke the name of a religious teacher. The view that art has become a sort of substitute for religion has been rejected by all serious critics. T. S. Eliot considered it one of the most insidious heresies of the nineteenth century. But the fact remains that in a godless age, and in what we call a free society, art is the only escape from materialism which is not subject to the law of diminishing returns, and one of the few which is not damaging to health. The moment of selfless joy which we experience in front of a work of art is no doubt less intense than the rapture of the saints. The most fervent art lovers have not yet undergone martyrdom. But artists like Gauguin have come near to it, and I think it would require something not far short of torture to make me deny that Cézanne was a good painter, whereas I have no views at all as to whether socialism or capitalism is the better economic system, and would cheerfully vote for either. Even if art is not strictly comparable to religion, it has become the chief focus of that part of human activity which, by a labor-saving linguistic shortcut, we may still call spiritual; and to lose our faith in it would be to create a dangerous void. Yet lose it we shall if we lose our sense of values and try to cover up the loss with metaphor and with endless researches into insignificant problems.

I think it is worth-while examining this situation, not with the hope that there is much we can do about it, because conditions of this kind have to work themselves out like the common cold, but because it is usually better to know where we stand in relation to the general historic process. There seem to be a number of factors involved, operating on various levels, which are probably all symptoms of the same general drift. The first of them can be described in one word: expansion. The existence of a clear, stable, and creative scale of values in art coincides with periods which are enclosed by a dome of clear and workable assumptions. All the great consistent styles have arisen in such periods. Occupied as we now are by differentiations and changes of fashion, we tend to overlook the underlying unity and long duration of such styles. We can see that little change took place in

Egyptian art for 2,500 years, and that the decorative clouds of the T'ang dynasty seem very similar to those of the Manchu emperors. When we look at Western European culture we are chiefly aware of the differences; and it is of course true that since the twelfth century the European mind has been possessed by a fearful restlessness, which before concentrating on science showed itself in art and architecture. But even so, the artificial and irrational forms invented in fifth-century Greece have proved as deeply rooted and as tenacious as anything in the Far East. The architectural idea of the Greek temple, a wooden chalet rendered in stone, might seem illogical enough to have faded out soon after its appearance. In fact, it had an unbroken existence for seven hundred years; and more than two thousand years after its invention it was still being used for the construction of temples by the very faith which had destroyed its original purpose. The Church of the Madeleine in Paris was finished 2,210 years after the Parthenon.

In such survivals there is, of course, an element of inertia. To discover and perfect a new form that shall impose itself on posterity requires colossal energy, as well as conviction. Nevertheless, such cultural survivals would not have been possible without a continuity of basic assumptions. The clear and workable assumptions which, till quite recently, controlled our scale of values, were not, as is sometimes supposed, Christian, but classical. After the Renaissance it was assumed that antiquity furnished a pattern for the arts, as it did for human behavior, and although there were rebels against the oppressive standards of classicism, it remained the norm. The first fluttering acceptance of medieval art was no more than embroidery on the surface of classic structure. As Pugin said of the Houses of Parliament, "All Grecian, sir. Tudor details on a classic body." The assimilation of the Gothic style, together with Chinoiserie, Turquerie, and Singerie, pierced the enclosed world of classical assumptions, but by the middle of the century critical historians like Charles Blanc and Eastlake had achieved a synthesis of values which still provided the hierarchy of taste on which most of us were brought up. Visitors to London may remember a curious structure, looking like a gigantic version of a Gothic ciborium, which was erected exactly a hundred years ago as a monument to the Prince Consort, husband of Queen Victoria. Albert had been a great patron of the arts, and round the

48

base of his memorial there was carved a marble frieze of painters, sculptors, architects, musicians, and writers. Of the 169 figures chosen by Eastlake to represent the arts in 1865 there is hardly one whose greatness and appropriateness we should question today (except that Delaroche appears instead of Delacroix). The artistic merits of the Albert Memorial are not usually rated very highly, but, in spite of the incursion of medieval art, the scale of values it proposes is comprehensive, stable, and convincing. The fact is that Gothic art was still the product of an evolved civilization; its philosophic method was still rational—extravagantly rational—and still looked back to Plato and Aristotle. The expansion of values which accompanied the Romantic Movement, although it had a questionable influence on architecture and the decorative arts, did not violate our sense of cultural unity. The real break came in the early years of this century when certain painters and critics found the qualities of great art in the work of primitive people. I am not denying that they did discover such qualities. The finest pieces of Negro or Polynesian carving are indeed great works of art. But the fact that we can feel this about the work of people with whose culture we have nothing in common, whose mental processes are almost wholly irrational and whose basic assumptions are entirely incomprehensible to us, represents a crucial change in our whole philosophy of art.

The discovery of primitive art was, at first, associated with a revolution in esthetics which had been brewing for some time. According to the new philosophy our response to works of art no longer involved a focus of intellectual and spiritual activities, but was a sensation, a kind of electric shock, unique and isolated from all other forms of experience. The merits of primitive art were a convenient illustration of this theory and were consequently much exaggerated. To this was soon added the discovery of children's art, which was supposed to be equally spontaneous and have a similar freedom from distracting associations. The discovery of monkeys' art belongs to a later phase of the same process and raises rather different questions.

I need not examine the fallacies inherent in this way of thought; they have become obvious enough. My point is that the vast expansion of what can be taken seriously as art led to a confusion of values, and the esthetic philosophy, of which it was the symptom, gave no indication of how this confusion might be resolved. To take a metaphor from another order of human experience, one may say that the artistic values of the eighteenth century were based on a kind of civil law, and when, in the mid-nineteenth century, this was stretched beyond its capacity, its place had been taken by a kind of natural law. This metaphor has the advantage that by 1850 the word "nature" had taken on an almost religious meaning. The "laws of nature," which in the eighteenth century had meant little more than probabilities based on normal experience, now meant to Ruskin, or, for that matter, to Walt Whitman, God's law for the conduct of the universe. This is the mental background of Constable's Wordsworthian nature worship, Courbet's realism, and the Impressionists' preoccupation with light. But they were still connected with the eighteenth-century laws by their confidence in the old humanist adage, frequently asserted by the first art-theorist of the Renaissance, Leon Battista Alberti, that "nature will always act consistently in all her operations."

In the present century this confidence was shattered by the expansion of the physical world—by the final incomprehensibility of the infinitely large and the infinitely small. It is a curious fact of history that whereas great artists have shown themselves uninfluenced by social or religious systems (minor artists, of course, have often conformed) they have always responded instinctively to latent assumptions about the shape of the universe. The medieval craftsman may have been almost illiterate, but his sense of space somehow reflects the logical complexities of Dantesque cosmogeny; the Renaissance artist conceived his forms, and situated them, in accordance with the measureable areas of Euclidian geometry; and when Galileo had established that the earth was no longer at the center of the universe, the vanishing point of pictorial perspective began to be placed outside the edge of the frame.

In all these epochs the universe seemed, if not comprehensible, at any rate realizable through some kind of symbolic projection. But quite early in the present century it became clear that no symbolic rendering of the universe could be close enough to the new data to have the smallest validity. As J. B. S. Haldane said, "My own suspicion is that the universe is not only queerer than we suppose, but queerer than we *can* suppose." Now, this feeling that the condition of the cosmos cannot even be stated symbolically and that, by our standards, it seems to be as incoherent as divine justice, was bound to have an effect on the sense of form and the sense of space. Kandinsky in his *Reminiscences* has left us a clear, though ultimately misleading, account of an artist's response to the triumph of contemporary physics. "The crumbling of the atom," he says, "was to my soul like the crumbling of the whole world. Everything became uncertain, tottering, weak. I would not have been surprised if a stone had dissolved in the air in front of me and become invisible." To understand the strength of Kandinsky's emotion we must remember the almost religious status which seventeenth century scientists had conferred on the atom. "So very hard," as Newton said, "as never to wear or break in pieces: no ordinary power being able to divide what God himself made one in the first creation." Kandinsky's memoirs were written in 1913, and in that year both Mosley and Niels Bohr had deprived the atom of some of its monomorphic dignity. No doubt their experiments were known to Kandinsky and seemed an exciting confirmation of his own pictorial needs. Nevertheless, I think that his statement is misleading, because he goes on to claim that this was the moment of liberation which allowed him to paint completely nonobjective pictures. "Science," he says, equating science with the laws of nature, "seemed to be destroyed. Its most important basis was only a delusion, an error of the learned." This is nonsense. Moreover Kandinsky had painted his first abstract pictures a year or two earlier, and the decisive influence was probably the French fauve painters of 1905–6. In studying the history of art the interplay between scientific or intellectual trends and what I may call professional movements within the arts themselves has to be treated with great caution; and some intoxicating analogies are best resisted. For example, Kandinsky's statement has encouraged writers on modern art to claim that there is an analogy between the splitting of the atom and the splitting up of the objective image. But, apart from chronological difficulties (and the anticipation of science by art is not unknown), this looks to me more like one of those word games which the hard-pressed critic finds convenient. The two processes exist in such different spheres of intellectual activity that they have very little, or nothing, in common.

The complete suppression of the external object came about when the esthetic philosophy of sensation attached to itself the epithet "pure." In 1913 Malevich produced his famous white square on a white ground and defended it with the words "by suprematism I understand the supremacy of *pure* feeling in creative art," adding "Everything that determines the objective ideal structure of life and of art—ideas, concepts and images—all this the artist has to cast aside in order to heed pure feeling." A few years later Mondrian extended this approach to a more intellectual idea of art, which he called "the mutual interaction of constructive elements and their internal relations." "This process," he says, "consists in mutual purification; purified constructive elements set up pure relationships, and then in their turn demand pure constructive elements."

You see that in my attempt to find out how a credible scale of values in art has been lost, I have been drawn into the problem of modern art. I would gladly have avoided a subject on which it seems to be almost impossible to say anything either sensible or new. Moreover, abstract art has been supported with such passionate loyalty that any attempt to view it with detachment is immediately interpreted as an attack. But in this study of values some reference to modern art is inevitable. Ultimately, it is the living art of our time and the personal tastes of dominant artists which redirect our appreciation of the past and govern what we call taste. In the past thirty years contemporary painting has played an active role in the liquidation of values by its constant change of aim. But through all the ups and downs of fashion, the main drift has been clear. It has been, and continues to be, toward an even greater abstraction, an even more rigorous suppression of the objective visual experience. Kandinsky, Malevich, and Mondrian remain the prophets of our present phase. Has anything like this happened before?

Well, as a matter of fact, it has. The iconophobic impulses, which both Byzantium and Islam took over from Judaic culture, although obviously different in many respects, show enough points of resemblance to be worth examining. For one thing they were primarily an esthetic phenomenon and appeared in art before they appeared in dogma. The heart had gone out of representational-figurative art in all the Syrian, Judaic, Coptic, and North African world before images were formally condemned by the church fathers and centuries before they were prohibited by Islam; and secondly, when image making was attacked it was in the name of *purity*. God is a spirit, to be apprehended immediately; and any attempt to represent him by an image, or even by a symbol, is to degrade the divine essence. I am not sure how far the author of the second commandment had this in mind: more probably he was simply anxious to preserve the unity of his tribe. But this was certainly the ideal of the church fathers of Syria, Africa, and Spain, and when it was abandoned by Gregory the Great, in about the year 600, we may say that the Roman Church had accepted that alliance with pagan antiquity which it has maintained till the present day. Of course, it would be a mistake to equate this early iconophobia with puritanism, as we have come to understand the word. The decoration of Saint Sophia, the most splendid church in Christendom, was originally without any figurative representations, and this was probably due to the influence of the Empress Theodora, who had been educated in Alexandria. No puritanism in her set. Equally, we cannot associate the ethos of the Pilgrim Fathers with that of the Caliphate, although both of them eschewed images. This Syrian iconophobia was based on purity of *sensation,* in which the sensuous immediacy of art gained force by being deprived of recognition and the complex train of associations which the figure arts arouse. But although we cannot call imageless art puritanical, we can properly call it anticatholic, something outside the main classical tradition and, to a large extent, something revolutionary, militant, and intolerant.

Cautiously examining the analogy between fourth–fifth-century iconophobia and modern art, we are struck with one important discrepancy. The imageless art of Syria, Egypt, and Constantinople was primarily decorative. Its effect on the human mind was subordinate to its function as part of an architectural whole. The capitals in the Coptic Museum in Cairo are great works of art, but they appeal, in the most narrow sense, to the esthetic emotions. They have practically no intellectual content and cannot be called a form of communication. This is a serious limitation and was felt to be so at the time: hence the inclusion, among the decorative motifs, of Christian symbols; and, in Islamic art, of texts from the Koran—although Cufic script is in itself so superbly decorative that this may be considered

53

cheating. Now, the nonrepresentational art of the past fifty years has vigorously denied the charge that it is decorative: and in its recent phases has claimed that it is essentially a communication. An apologist of tachism has said, "What we want to know is not what the world looks like, but what we mean to each other": obvious enough in tachism; but even the most austere constructions of abstract art express personal convictions. We often say in criticism of someone's character that "he lacks a sense of proportion," and when this trite metaphor is given concrete and visible form we must accept it as a true communication of personality.

But in spite of this serious discrepancy, the points of likeness are considerable and, I think, valid. The most striking is the insistence on purity. I have already given examples from the prophets of modern painting; I may add to them the prophet of modern music, Arnold Schoenberg. In his opera *Moses and Aaron,* which he thought of as his crowning achievement, Moses the exponent of the pure word of God is betrayed by his brother, who believes that the word must be revealed through images. It was Schoenberg's intention to end the opera with the triumph of Moses, but he could think of no conclusive arguments and the third act was never written. Perhaps only Spinoza could have provided an adequate libretto.

This notion that a spiritual experience, whether received through the senses or through the intellect, must be pure, although psychologically an exceedingly dubious concept, has had a recurring fascination for the European mind, and has often (Cistercians, Quakers, etc.) led to the suppression of ornament as well as of images. Perhaps we may say that modern architecture is to some extent a reflection of this state of mind. In modern painting it became involved with other factors— the vulgar rivalry of the camera and exhaustion of nineteenth-century academism. All these factors combined to make it an art of revolt against the conforming center; and since for over fifty years almost every movement which was at first attacked or derided was later valued and praised, the idea has taken root that to be ultimately valuable a work of art must be initially shocking. A certain amount of modern art cannot really be accounted for on any other principle. Needless to say, there is nothing in the history of art earlier than 1860 to support this view, and I would not mention anything so ephemeral were it not certain that this unconscious argument has played a part in the formation of contemporary taste.

Since the conventional view of painting was, and perhaps still is, that it should represent objective reality, and since academic art was encumbered by a repertoire of trivial observations, it was natural that an art of revolt should feel bound to purify itself from the detritus of normal perception, and the drift of fashion coincided with the more profound urge toward purity and abstraction.

I have elsewhere suggested a third reason for the specialized character of modern art, the ascendancy of science. I am now inclined to question how far this theory is valid. It is true that in the Middle Ages and the Renaissance science and art were much closer together than they are today, because one of the functions of art was to convey information about the visible world; and as science became more specialized and drew away from normal means of perception this unity (with many others) was inevitably lost. But one must admit that science was already specialized in the nineteenth century, and the nineteenth century produced a quantity of great artists. However, I think it is true to say that as science has become more specialized and more abstract, so art has felt the need to make its own realm purer and more inaccessible. To anticipate a discovery of physics by a mathematical equation is a feat of intelligence which seems to require of art something more than mere observation.

Such then would be my summary of our present situation, and if it is correct you will see why modern art has contributed to our uncertainty of values. The word "pure," although very far from precise when applied to a work of art, is not without a shadow of meaning. It implies that the work in question affects us primarily through its form and color, and that the elements of memory and association which it contains are so completely absorbed in the form and color that we are only aware of them unconsciously. To take a concrete instance, we may say that a Matisse collage is "purer" than a Matisse odalisque, meaning that in the collage the odalisque has been swallowed, although she can be recognized in the curves of a piece of blue paper by those who know Matisse's earlier work. Evidently the "purer" an art becomes the less easily can it be judged by ordinary human standards. The more a spiritual experience becomes immediate the less it is

55

dependent on tradition. As I have said, modern art is, in a large sense of the word, anticatholic. Not only does it abandon that alliance with the physical world and that need to digest every scrap of human experience which has nourished the Catholic Church; but historically it has been promoted by artists from outside the nursery of traditional art, the northern shores of the Mediterranean. Two of its founders and several of its chief living representatives come from a country which was supposed to have no tradition of painting at all, from Russia; and it seems to me doubtful if abstract art would have lasted so long if it had not taken root in the virgin soil of the United States of America. (Let me hasten to add that I am not forgetting the very considerable American artists of the nineteenth century. But neither Eakins nor Winslow Homer can be said to have been at the creative center of the art in their time; whereas the abstract painters of New York are.)

Now, tradition is without doubt the most comfortable source of values and the old Catholic maxim *securus judicat orbis terrarum* is still a first step toward understanding. At all times tradition saves one a lot of anxiety, and never more than at a time when matter is changing its composition and the universe its shape in a way that very few of us can understand, but with results which all of us have reason to dread. And yet we know that to pretend to believe in a dead tradition is one of the least fruitful forms of pretense. *Orbis terrarum* meant simply the Mediterranean, and our secure judgments must be based on something very much wider.

Where can we find a new basis of value? What, in the expanding universe, have we got left? We have ourselves. It is through human qualities, after all, that man has extended himself beyond his own comprehension, through his memory, his ability to draw inferences, his willingness to cooperate, and his imagination. All over the world men have the same needs, the same means of perception, and the same emotions. They respond to the same rhythms and dream the same dreams. The discovery of primitive art, which did so much to shake the values of the classical tradition, is also one of the most moving proofs of the unity of mankind. Thus the problem of values becomes a problem of interpretation. We can perceive in the arts of every culture certain qualities of form, of design, of esthetic purpose which seem to transcend differences of social and economic organization; and these formal qualities must, in the end, be the visible expression of human experience. It is our duty to interpret them. We cannot all read an abstract work of art as Ruskin could read a Byzantine capital or as Riegl could follow the evolution of the palmette; but with a little help we can come much nearer to it than we suppose. The very metaphors of popular speech show an amazing power of abstraction. We have no difficulty in recognizing weakness or strength, nobility, or meanness in the shape of a pot, if it is pointed out to us. This leads me back to a point I touched on earlier, the responsibility of art historians for the collapse of values. As the old humanist tradition became untenable they abandoned the function of criticism or evaluation, giving as their excuse the amount of research still to be done on the available evidence. It is true that we have collected a formidable quantity of evidence. Our museums are stuffed to capacity, far beyond the needs of the average visitor; and photography has added a mountain of documentation, convenient and deceptive. But sooner or later the pleasant ritual of classification, with its small certainties, must give place to the labor of analysis and the hazards of synthesis. We need great historical interpreters of form like Ruskin, Riegl, Wolfflin, Dvořák, and Focillon.

I say "historical" because only by grouping and analyzing the art of the past can we recognize those elements which are lasting and universal; and I say "form" because, in the study of mankind, subject divides, form unites. The fact that all over the world, and at every stage of culture, men have felt a need to impose forms of order on the chaos of visible experiences, and that we can recognize the value of these forms intuitively, without knowing anything about the circumstances that produced them, should be reckoned one of the great discoveries of the past fifty years. The appreciation of primitive art, which seemed at first to have contributed to the displacement of values, should in the end be the basis of a new humanism. Unfortunately, the esthetic theory which accompanied this discovery, the notion that this universally valid sense of form must be a sensation unconnected with other human experiences, was an error. No doubt there will always be in our response to works of art some physical feelings that will resist analysis: the scent of the rose. It was Ruskin himself who said "sculpture is essentially the production of a bossiness or pleasant roundness." But to call this physical quality "pure" and to claim that it alone is the source of esthetic pleasure is a fallacy. Even the most primitive art is suffused with human emotions. In a recent exhibition of Negro carvings in Paris, I was struck less by the plastic qualities which had so forcibly impressed the painter of the Demoiselles d'Avignon than by their nobility and pathos.

The critical point in all interpretation is precisely the point at which experience becomes form; and it is as elusive as the moment when we actually fall asleep. But what should we say of a biologist who gave up further investigations because the secret of life was said to be impenetrable? Of course, the art historian's work has become more complex, not only on account of the accumulation of evidence but also because of the more elaborate tests to which works of art must be submitted. If we allow that the creative moment is modified by innumerable memories and associations, then we must use, in our analysis, all the analogies that can help us through this uncharted sea. Symbol and gesture, ritual and play, mythology and psychology, patterns of animal behavior, all these must be related to works of art, not merely to unriddle subjects, but to elucidate form. At the end of it all we shall find out only what we know already by instinct. But we shall at least have produced ammunition to use against the present uneasy skepticism which has shaken our sense of value.

IAN McTAGGART COWAN

Ian McTaggart Cowan, distinguished Canadian ecologist and conservationist, was born in Edinburgh, Scotland, on June 25, 1910. He received his B.A. from the University of British Columbia in 1932 and his Ph.D. from the University of California in 1935.

In 1929 Cowan worked as an insect-pest investigator for the Canadian Government and a year later became a field assistant for the National Museum of Canada. His next position was as a teaching fellow at the University of California from 1932 to 1935. Returning to Canada in 1935, he became assistant biologist in the British Columbia Provincial Museum and in 1938 was promoted to assistant director. He stayed there two more years before joining the University of British Columbia as assistant professor of zoology. He became professor in 1945, head of the department in 1953, assistant dean of arts and sciences in 1957, and dean of the faculty of graduate studies in 1964.

Dr. Cowan was a Carnegie Traveling Fellow with the American Museum of Natural History and the United States National Museum in 1937 and a Nuffield Fellow in 1952. He has served with the Dominion Parks Bureau (consulting biologist, National Parks of Canada) and the Northwest Territories Administration and is a fellow of the Royal Society of Canada. In 1949 he became president of the [American] Wildlife Society. He is also a member of the Fisheries Research Board of Canada, the National Research Council of Canada, the American Ornithologists' Union, and the American Society of Mammalogists.

Not only is Dr. Cowan dean of the graduate faculty at the University of British Columbia, but he is also an international dean of nature conservation. He has set a fine example as a basic scientist with a strong sense of public responsibility in speaking out for conservation policies. As coauthor of a committee on national parks of the Wildlife Society in 1963, he helped formulate contemporary principles for managing our national parks. Other countries look to this document as a basic guide in policy for their national parks.

As a scientist, Cowan has published about 200 papers on a wide variety of subjects including speciation in western deer; diseases of wild animals; the dynamics of populations and ecology of native sheep, elk, and deer in Banff and Jasper National Parks of Canada; and genetic growth rates and nutrition of deer in captivity.

In his busy life as a university teacher and administrator, he has found time to appear on the Canadian Broadcasting Corporation educational television series called "The Web of Life." He is constantly in demand in the United States and Canada for lecturing; conducting symposia at scientific conferences; and advising government agencies, universities, and foundations on matters of education, scientific research, and conservation.

Conservation
and Man's Environment

IAN McTAGGART COWAN

THROUGH THE MILLENNIA of his birth, man was a poorly equipped, struggling omnivore inhabiting environments that offered special favor. Populations were small, and the product of a limited area was the sole support of its humans. As man the inventor, however, he added to his inadequate physical attributes a long series of devices that extended his ability as a food gatherer and expanded his environmental tolerance. With increasing competence, the itinerant hunter–food gatherer in his family group became the neolithic agriculturist. This was certainly subsistence agriculture, but it permitted the first permanent settlements and therewith the first truly man-made environments. The discovery of the river basins with their rich soils led later to the production of food surpluses and with these the specialists, the villages, and later the cities.

Through these years when every man was an intimate daily participant in the struggle to wrest survival from an unpredictable environment, a rich store of folk images grew from the day to day experiences. These guided his biological routines and provided acceptable explanations for the commonplace physical and biological phenomena. He was an observant and rational creature, and here and there across the world developed some effective practices to prolong the food-producing ability of his habitat. These folk techniques, however, were family or tribal in scope and died with the group. In general, early man lacked a concern for the environment, for the creatures in it, and for the consequences of man's activity. Great cities were born in the Mediterranean basin and elsewhere, many to be abandoned in a few hundred years as desolate monuments to man's ineptitude. Climatic change has been proposed as explanation for these early failures of urban man. The overwhelming weight of evidence, however, points clearly to man, not climate, as the agency that let in the desert, or destroyed the capability of the soil.

Then, scarcely a century ago, he turned his talents to vital inventions. Aseptic surgery, vaccination, public-health measures, antibiotics, and chemotherapy introduced a new era in which man emerged as the first creature to directly influence the answers to the ageless questions—who dies, when, and of what? The outcome of these discoveries is clearly revealed in the burgeoning human populations.

It was the thought processes of science that consolidated the era of vital invention and started man on the harried course to large-scale environmental manipulation. The scientific image emerged, frequently in sharp conflict with the folk image of the living world and its relationships. As Boulding has pointed out, even a relatively imperfect shift from the folk image of man and society to a scientific image involves man in at least two large, irreversible, and related changes. The first of these is the increase in self-consciousness, not only of the individual himself, but also of the society in which he has been placed. The second change is the development of the integrated systems point of view, where the world is seen as functioning in an orderly and predictable way, where imposed changes have predictable consesequences.

Man is no longer the frail primate, surrounded on every hand by baleful and mysterious forces, wild beasts, and pestilence. He glories in his new capacity to go where he wills when he wishes, to conquer all natural obstacles, to guide his own star. We have man the despoiler, the casual pursuer of short-term goals, the arbiter of survival for so much of the world's biota. At the same time, this is man the creator of majestic works, self-conscious man, the only moral creature, man the conservator ready to answer for his errors and to extend the umbrella of his competence over many lesser forms of life with which he shares his environment.

This, to me, is one of the great revolutions of attitude of all time; man the fearful becomes man the master.

THE ROOTS OF CONSERVATION

Conservation as we know it today is a complicated and interesting area of activity. In very large part it is the expression of the enlightened self-interest of a population arising from the understanding, scientifically gained, of the laws of growth, the known facts of population regulation, and the discovery that for wild crops, as for tame, the environment has a capacity which it cannot exceed but can sustain.

This is conservation as it is properly applied to the living, self-replacing resources upon which man can draw for his sustenance, his energy needs, and his economic enrichment. The doctrine of wise use is the operating principle. Properly stated, it is that a living resource may not be used at a rate faster than its capacity to replace itself. Sustained yield is the objective of the management programs in forestry, in fisheries, and in wildlife management. In these areas of conservation self-consciousness is happily bolstered by the profit motive. It profits man in the long run to conserve the renewable resources.

The evolution of the principle of sustained yield has its roots in the folk learning of antiquity, given form, substance, and conceptual veracity by science. It first received public acknowledgment as the operating framework of a national policy when, in 1910, President Theodore Roosevelt promulgated what has come to be known as the Roosevelt Doctrine. This recognized all outdoor resources as an inseparable whole, established the public responsibility for the wise use of these resources, and declared science as the working instrument to guide public policy.

But though the Roosevelt Doctrine marked the inauguration of the era of scientific conservation, it was itself the outcome of half a century of struggle acted out in the political arena of the United States as the old concepts of the private right to all public resources were defeated in the devastated forest lands of America, and the role of water on the arid lands of the central continent became established in law. The names of Carl Schurz, United States Secretary of the Interior under President Hayes, and of John Wesley Powell are prominent among those who saw the message of conservation boldly

63

written in a troubled landscape nearly a century ago. But, as usual, reason was slow in acceptance, as its adversary was the easy short-term profit where wealth and political influence were bedfellows.

In almost every instance it was born of human tragedy; ghost towns in a chaos of ravished forest land, towering clouds of topsoil that carried with them the hopes of thousands in Oklahoma and the other dustbowl areas of the world, surging flood waters on the delta lands, stinking rivers carrying sickness to all who used them. Always the task faced by the ecologist in conservation has been to rescue man from the consequences of ignorance, avarice, or folly.

The continent is still repaying the debt that was ruthlessly extracted from the landscape in the nineteenth century. "In the forests, as on the ranges and in the mines, it was every man for himself, and it would take a generation of protest, and a Rough Rider President, to slow down the onslaught and put the get-rich-quick capitalists on the defensive. The nineteenth-century lumber tycoons, to give them full credit, housed a growing nation, cleared land, and hastened the pace of westward expansion. However, in the process, they set world records for waste, and their prodigal prosperity consumed the stored 'capital' of nature—which, by right, belonged to other generations."[1]

The other parent of today's conservation takes its origin from more complicated sources. Moral conscience offended by killing beyond need, religious concepts of cruelty, and a genuine concern to retain for our enjoyment creatures whose beauty of color, form, movement, and sound appeal to the senses and give us pleasure. The protectionist movement has its roots as deep in human antiquity as art, music, and religion. In its earliest manifestations it is a folk movement strongly espoused by an ever-enlarging segment of our society. However, along the way, it is gaining the strength of true understanding derived from scientific inquiry and the unarguable power of the market place. People will pay for it!

This aspect of conservation was at first concerned with the protection of birds by the establishment of refuges, but it rapidly broadened to encompass the preservation of entire areas of special beauty or unique biota. The national park concept emerged as one of the most powerful popular movements of our time.

Perhaps the dominant trend in conservation today arises out of our growing realization of the influence human populations have already had on their environment. If indeed we seek mastery of our fate, of fundamental importance is control of ourselves and regulation of our actions as degraders of the potential contribution that environments may make to future generations. The frontier philosophy of do what most profits without thought for tomorrow is no longer tolerated as a working principle by any advanced society.

It is near thirty years since Aldo Leopold gave expression to the "ecological conscience," recognizing each generation not as owners outright of the land and its resources but the holders of life rent with the responsibility of wise custodianship without reduction in potential. Ecologists have been slow to involve themselves with a study of man as the dominant influence in the world's terrestrial ecosystems. But, even so, our knowledge of human ecology is growing rapidly, paced by such exhaustive summaries as the Wenner-Gren Foundation report, *Man's Role in Changing the Face of the Earth,*[2] the searching studies of the British scene by Nature Conservancy; and the recent conference on the "Future Environments of North America."[3] As the understanding of the ecologists increases, so also does appreciation of our potential for actions detrimental to human environment.

The complex web of man's impact on his environment defies neat compartmentalization, but there are five areas that by virtue of differing group interest and research-need justify separate comment: (1) Soil conservation; (2) the role of man in the survival of the biota or of its productive capacity; (3) the ecology of man-made pollution; (4) the maintenance of natural beauty and the opportunity to relate to nature; and (5) the maintenance of genetic variety and the preservation of opportunity to learn.

SOIL CONSERVATION

Here and there in time and location man has gleaned bits of information on the nurture of the soil as he extracted his crops from the arid lands or sought his livelihood on the steepening hillsides of an overcrowded habitat. The great drought period of the 1930's in central North America, however, for the first time found man ready for massive, effective, science-based attack on the soil problems of a continent. The Soil Conservation Service of the United States established under Franklin Roosevelt's administration can fairly claim to have changed the face of a continent in its thirty years of existence. In so doing it has mustered an understanding and a technical force that are carrying their influence to many lands.

Soil conservation in North America has made possible the tremendous food-producing potential of the continent, but beyond this it has had immeasurable influence on all other aspects of natural resource conservation.

CONSERVATION OF SPECIES

The expansion of natural history into ecology during the scientific revolution saw the principles upon which the idea of conservation rests added to abundantly, both at the operating level and in concept. The community as a vital entity operating in accord with discernible laws that could yield prediction and the idea of the limiting factor, and of density dependent feedback between organism and environment, were among those hypotheses that provided new conceptual equipment.

The idea of altering the natural forces that were regulating the lives of creatures other than ourselves is a major landmark in the flowering of human ideas, and its emergence marked the transition between simple protection and management: the purposeful attempt to alter the environmental impact on a species or community to produce a preconceived result. Management includes the regulation of the direct or indirect impact of man on the species or community, as well as all attempts to alter such other features of the environment as water, food, shelter, parasites, disease, predation, special facilities, competition, or distribution. The objective of management in conservation today is much broader than the mere maximizing of profit. Each living organism is seen as the repository of a unique assortment of biological information gained through the eras via the process of evolution. Each offers a potential enrichment of human knowledge and enjoyment that is limited only by our capacity to appreciate. The loss of any single

66

element in the world's store of varied life is viewed as an erosion of the quality of the human environment.

In general terms, management is directed to the encouragement of those species we desire to assist, to reduce populations of creatures we regard as damaging our interests, or to maintain the integrity of an entire assembly of plants and animals; that is, to maintain a community for its riches of species and associations. Species-oriented conservation falls into three main categories: Management for survival; management of distribution; and management for harvest.

MANAGEMENT FOR SURVIVAL

In nineteen hundred years the world has lost 107 kinds of mammals and close to 100 kinds of birds. The extent of extinction of plants and the lesser animals is not known but probably vastly exceeds that of birds and mammals. Nearly 70 percent of these losses have occurred in the past century and mostly through the activity of man. Here and there throughout the world, on every continent and on many of the remotest islands, a host of other species, more than 1,000 strong, face the imminence of complete and final passage from the world's fauna.

Extinction has been an essential companion of evolution since the beginning of time, and there is no reason to believe that the process is complete. None the less, it is an ideal of conservation that no creature should pass from the face of the earth through the instrumentality of man. If we would pose as the masters of creation, to prevent extermination of a large and obvious form of life stands as a challenge to our ingenuity and our competence.

There is an element of drama also in the plight of a vanishing creature that captures the imagination. The challenge to aid the troubled species thus has consequences far beyond the retention of its genotype. It becomes an instrument of enlightenment as thousands of people develop an increased awareness of the principles of conservation through identification with the endeavor.

Several special agencies make their particular concern the assembly of all available data upon endangered species. The International Union for the Protection of Birds, the Survival Service Commission of the International Union for the Conservation of Nature, as well as many agencies of Western governments, Japan, and several European nations contribute in important degree to the identification of species in trouble and in coordinating assistance programs. The International Union and the World Wildlife Fund muster the skills and organize the support for emergency attempts to redress the havoc man has wrought upon wildlife in the farthest corners of the world. In the United States the recent Land and Water Conservation Fund Act provides for the protection of endangered species. There are substantial successes, but the tasks are huge and without precedent. Species that are in trouble as an outcome of man's alterations of habitat have proved most difficult to assist, as have insular endemics. Long periods of evolution out of contact with the specialized competitors, predators, and diseases of the continents have rendered island species most vulnerable to the impact of man-induced changes in environment. Islands are unique and desperately fragile. They require special care. Introductions of exotics, domestic species, or of diseases are almost certain to be catastrophic.

It is impossible to foresee the direction that our interests in the biota will take as human tenure of the earth lengthens, as our populations increase, our demands upon the resources expand, and our understanding of the environment becomes ever more detailed. Today our concern is for the forest trees, certain more obvious plants, and for the mammals, birds, some fishes, and some reptiles. Our knowledge of the ecological facts pertinent to the management of most of these is inadequate, and we are totally innocent of the data that would permit us to manage the populations of most of the living creatures of the world. The only tenable approach to the maintenance of the largest part of the biota is through the management of ecosystems rather than individual species.

Where climax situations are concerned the task, in theory, is relatively simple. On the other hand, the restoration and maintenance of any of the transitory seral stages in a living community of plants and animals constitute a task of great complexity, so much so that we are at present almost powerless to plan for the successful ecological management of even the smaller national parks of this continent.

The usual approach to the conservation of vanishing plants or animals has been to create a refuge or park to contain it and to exclude fire. Special reserved areas have been established to maintain stands of climax redwood forest, Douglas firs, Monterey cypresses, organ-pipe cactuses, Joshua trees, and the entire flora of some of the Hawaiian craters. These measures are seldom adequate, and the truly ecological view of the objectives is only beginning to enter into planning and administration.

MANAGEMENT OF DISTRIBUTION

In general, a species becomes less vulnerable as its distribution widens. Discontinuity of distribution is of special importance as it protects against the inadvertent catastrophe that can overwhelm a single small population.

We can sometimes foster discontinuity of distribution by carefully selected transplants of a species into unoccupied but apparently suitable habitat.

This, at the same time, provides a unique opportunity for the establishment of a disease-free nucleus population. Natural extinction has been an active process through all existence. Although we have little knowledge of the causes of extinction, epizootic disease is a possibility. Thus the establishment of disease-free discontinuous populations should give added survival value to the species and will provide additional surety to our objective of management for variety.

MANAGEMENT FOR HARVEST

In general, the utilization of a new element in the biological resource still follows the primitive pattern. Thus for each new species for which we find a use there occurs first a period of uninhibited exploitation, as if the resource was unlimited. Sooner or later, declining availability arouses concern that the stock will be commercially eliminated. Too frequently, the rising cash value emerging from progressive scarcity obscures the biological situation and renders politically difficult the establishment of measures adequate to restore the productivity of the resource and to place it on a basis of sustained yield management.

Conservation practices designed to manage for sustained yield consist of fact-finding, restrictive regulation, and positive management. The important difference between the last two is that, while restrictive regulation is designed to regulate human exploitation of a wild species to a level at or below the mean replacement rate, positive management is oriented toward increasing the production or survival of young and to lengthening the life of adults of the managed species. In terms of the classical sigmoid of population growth the objective of conservation of a harvested population is to maintain the population at the level of greatest rate of increase while at the same time moving this upward by raising the ceiling imposed by the environment.

Most wild populations exist within a delicately balanced complex of species that make mutual use of the food potential of the environment. Some competition between species is frequent. The consequence of human depletion of certain species is often to promote a new balance within which the preferred species plays a lesser role. A biological vacuum often does not arise, and for this reason it may be impossible to restore the population to its early productivity even under the best of management.

Where the demand is greatest, the concept of maximum sustainable yield has come into being. This may be expressed in terms of numbers, weight, or cash return.

The simpler task of sustained yield management is that confronting the forester whose product is wood. His populations are immobile and easily measured, and the regulation of size of harvest presents few biological problems of decision. The unique factors are the long period of growth between harvests and, in the north, the vast areas of almost single species forests. These render protection from fire and pestilence the major hazards to success and the technology of these tasks becomes limiting.

Increasingly, the value of many forests arises not from their primary product but from their contribution to maintaining the integrity of watersheds, as an environment for wildlife, as a wilderness, and as a place for human recreation. Here the designation of goals is more difficult, and the knowledge demanded for successful management more precise. In only a few areas is adequate research information available.

Few among the world's fishes provide commercially important harvests and for only a handful of species can it be claimed that effective, sustained yield management is in force. In many instances our biological ignorance is inhibiting the development of management routines. For more of the marine fishes the political complications of the multinational competition for the crop frustrate the application of even existing information to the task of conservation.

The principle of abstention that is being pioneered with respect to certain of the North Pacific fisheries is a useful experiment in international conservation. Under this Canada, Japan, and the United States have agreed to abstain from fishing stocks of fish under full use and scientific management by any one of them. To be effective, however, agreements of this sort require the participation of all those nations that are competing for the fish resource of the management area. An important effect of such an agreement is the incentive for additional studies and better management.

The worst example of the failure of conservation, not for want of biological information but from bad faith, commercial avarice, and political iniquity, is to be seen in our treatment of the marine mammals of the world. Completely adequate demonstration has been available for at least a decade that species after species among the larger whales is being reduced to the point of extinction, and the industrial potential of the industry thus destroyed. Despite this, the responsible international organization of whaling nations has been repeatedly prevented from establishing the essential conservation measures through the political influence wielded by certain commercial interests bent only on retiring an investment as quickly as possible.

THE ECOLOGY OF POLLUTION

The most insidious influences of man in the environment arise from the disposal of wastes and from the purposeful distribution of biocide chemicals to destroy plants, insects, and related organisms regarded as inimical to certain human activities. These two forms of activity have the common denominator of so altering the environment chemically or physically that it is no longer a suitable habitat for many native forms of life and is often damaged as a habitat for man himself.

71

Egler has stated that "the problem of pesticides in the human environment is 95 percent a problem—not in the scientific knowledge of pesticides, not in the scientific knowledge of the environment—but in the scientific knowledge of human behavior"[4]: A combination of apathy and organized stupidity frequently motivated by the market place. The same can be said for pollution in the more usual sense. The devastating consequences of the ecological ignorance that fosters and permits such action was realistically presented to millions of people the world over by Rachel Carson in *Silent Spring*.[5]

Again to quote Egler: "In general, we have acted with remarkable arrogance to the whole-nature of which we are a part. Any part we do not want, we seek to destroy, completely and utterly . . . With the destruction of each such 'pest' by the use of the handiest, cheapest, most quickly acting 'pesticide,' goes the destruction of anything else about which we do not care at the moment, or the eventual destruction of other things about which we may care, but by such remote side-effects that the actual connection can be disputed."[4]

The problem is of world-wide scope and increases with the rise of human populations, but it is most intense in the sophisticated societies with the most advanced chemical industries.

Despite the growing public awareness that there are grave consequences from our present introduction of destructive chemicals into the ecosystem, the manufacture and distribution of these are increasing annually. There is no limit to our ingenuity in designing new forms in which we can introduce chemicals into the complicated web of our ecosystems, while we are powerless to influence where they will travel and impotent to remove them.

The biological destruction of rivers and lakes through the introduction into them of sewage and the chemical effluent of industry has aroused widespread public concern. The problem has become a national emergency in many countries and has generated powerful corrective efforts. Despite local success the pollution of fresh waters remains one of the most devastating consequences of civilization. Nowhere else in our relationship with the biological world in which we live are the lines of our understanding, our communication, our sources of political action, our economic ambitions, our biases, and our fears more hopelessly interwoven. It is difficult not to despair that an economic society is impotent to prevent the pollution of land, air, and water which we now support or condone.

Viewed the world over, mankind today is indeed managing his environment. This management, however, is not the outcome of a studied attempt to proceed toward a desired objective; it is rather the cumulative result of varied extemporizing, unplanned and uncoordinated, directed toward the satisfaction of the immediate need. Individuals, societies, and governments frequently compete and promote conflicting attitudes and acts of strong environmental consequence. We are completely without any well-defined and generally accepted philosophy to direct our specific behavior toward our surroundings.

Even our governments are not organized to react effectively to a comprehensive management of our actions as they influence the human biophysical environment. We are geared for local crises, the epidemic, the crop failure, the forest fire, the devastation of riparian lowlands by flood, which all trigger prompt action by some appropriate authority. These are crises easily seen and understood, dramatic in their impact on our immediate desires. The environmental changes of the greater ultimate importance take place so gradually, insidiously, and unobtrusively that they escape our attention until irreparable harm is done. Cumulative contamination of the environment by the waste products of our factories, kitchens, and bathrooms; gradual destruction of wildlife habitats with all they contain; the sprawling blight that flows from our cities farther and farther into the countryside; the indestructible wastes of our technology—beer can after auto-carcass, plastic bottle after pliofilm bag, spreading filth over our beauty spots—these have not yet reached that point in public understanding where consensus can lead to effective corrective action.

MAN AND THE ENJOYMENT RESOURCES

The world of today falls, perhaps loosely, into two categories of human societies. There are those which, despite improvements in scattered technologies, are concerned, at the level of the average individual, with the day-to-day task of staying alive. For them, it can be truly said that the immediate objectives and concepts have changed little since the days of human origin. The concern is living, not the quality of life. At the other extreme are those fortunate societies that have evolved through science and social ingenuity a competence that has to a very large extent banished the folk fears of starvation and pestilence and introduced new horizons to the image of life. Concern has shifted to the richness of experience that any individual can expect from his environment. It has become a proper objective of all mankind as far as possible to equalize the opportunity available to all individuals in all societies. There is no gain for man, however, if equalization is downward.

The logical concomitant of this principle is that those societies that have progressed farthest in the search for quality of living should exercise a concern extending far beyond their borders. Mankind's tomorrow will be found on the world scene, not within the parochial confines of a contemporary political unit. The contribution to the food stocks and to the economic potential of a country that is to be found in its renewable consumptive resources makes these obvious first candidates for attention. But, as Sir Julian Huxley has so well said, "Human ecology involves finding out what resources are available in our environments and how to make best use of them. We have to think first of all the material resources—minerals, water power, soil, forests, agricultural production—but we must also think of the non-material or enjoyment resources of the habitat, such as natural beauty and solitude, interest and adventure, wild scenery and wildlife . . . We should set about planning a Fulfillment Society rather than a Welfare Society, an Efficiency Society, or a Power Society."[6]

It can safely be said that one of the important criteria of an advanced society is its devotion to the maintenance of the ecological wellbeing of the human environment in all its attributes. Prominent among these will be the nonconsumptive uses for recreational enjoyment and scientific enrichment.

The recognition of the deep need of man for opportunity to associate himself with nature first occurred as a revulsion from the stark surroundings of the factory environment that became the lot of the majority during the Industrial Revolution. The easily accessible commons, though not yet recognized as such—for psychiatrists were as unknown as jet propulsion—became for the toiling thousands of Britain psychiatric safety valves.

A century ago, the land-grabbing aristocracy of Britain, who had already taken to themselves one acre of every seven in the nation, attempted to enclose Wimbledon and Epsom Commons. This was the touchstone to a legal battle of classical import. Henry Fawcett, M.P. and professor of political economy at Cambridge, championed the cause and saw in it the great principle that was at issue—the public right to open space reserved in its name. The legal battle was fought between the Corporation of London and fourteen Lords of Manors who sought to divide Epping Forest. The Corporation won the suit and established the all-important legal principle upon which so much of our more recent conservation legislation has rested. The Act of 1876 permanently declared in Britain the public interest in open spaces as taking precedence over private desires. Since 1925 British law has given to the public a statutory right of access for air and exercise on every common or place of manorial waste and to any rural common.[7]

An ocean away the practical dreamers of the New World were forming ideas of similar philosophy. With the expansiveness of thinking that accompanied the great spaces, American concepts spread from such fine civic beauty spots as New York's Central Park to California's Yosemite and the magnificent two million acres of the first National Park—Yellowstone. All this before 1875. The first voices also were decrying two and a half centuries devoted to plundering the natural resources of North America. The buffalo herds were gone as were the vast flocks of passenger pigeons, but worse, none had successfully challenged the view that the natural wealth of the biological resources was free for the taking, and to this the continent's devastated forests were prime testimony.

It took the combination of a brilliant, visionary forester, Gifford Pinchot, and Theodore Roosevelt, a President of the United States with deep roots in the wilderness, to turn the tide and to introduce the concepts of conservation. Among the first large-scale tangible results was the establishment of the great national forest system of the United States. Designed to produce timber for the long-time good of the nation, these forests now contribute richly to the recreational lands of the continent. None in the New World could then foresee the crowded cities, the airports, superhighways, the clatter, speed, and tensions to come, and the desperate need of people to find themselves again in the impersonality of unspoiled landscapes, in the surging vitality of many small lives.

"Modern man is turning almost instinctively to the last remnants of the primeval scene, to know again the mystery of the unknown and the beauties of unchanged terrain. While it is doubtful if his ancestors appreciated the intangible qualities of wild country, he is developing that capacity. Now that wilderness is no longer a threat to security or survival, he is beginning to look at it for the first time with some measure of appreciation and understanding, realizing that within it may be the answer to confusion and a source of inspiration closely allied to beauty. . . . National Parks, as reservations of beauty, are sanctuaries where people may recapture at least in part, some glimmer of the visions that may have stirred their forebears."[8]

With pathetic frequency our groping hands have left irreparable scars on the beauty we sought to serve. Superhighways, garbage dumps, golf courses, hydro-electric impoundments, cattle grazing, mining, and deforesting are only a few of the incongruous and destructive activities we have condoned in our parks, but we have hammered out some principles along the way:

1. On the world scene the national park concept has usefully served many objectives. The most frequent has been the preservation of endangered species where this depends upon intact segments of entire ecosystems. A new and exciting concept has emerged on the American continent. National parks, as we now view them, may have great value as museums of ecology, as wildlife reserves, archeological sites, or for the protection of wilderness and other natural wonders, but their first function is to provide the setting, the beauty, timelessness, and natural order in which man can regain the perspective he needs.

2. The national parks belong to all people, and no part of the policy that guides their operation should be oriented to provide private profit to local residents.

3. An attested ecological objective to guide park policy is an essential. The Leopold Committee urges that this be to retain or restore the ecological conditions obtaining when the region was discovered.

4. Protection of park values from increasing hordes of users is among the most challenging problems today. Zoning for

quality of use and the limitation of access are growing necessities.

5. The social organization requisite to the protection of State or Provincial parks whose policy and survival can be altered on executive whim has so far eluded our political ingenuity. On the American continent where the political voice of the entrepreneur is loudest the integrity of all parks requires the constant vigilance of militant citizen groups.

6. For the economically oriented, it has been shown beyond doubt that well-managed national parks pay dividends beyond their operating costs and may, as in parts of Africa, form the basis of a major industry.

MAINTENANCE OF GENETIC VARIETY

At this point the conservation road forks again into the scientific and the esthetic. With or without our consent, the evolutionary process will continue, new forms will arise and others vanish, most of them without our ken. The advent of man introduced a new and dominant force into the biosphere. By his selection as by his modification of the environment he has greatly altered the tempo and nature of evolutionary change. It is certain that the practical consequences of the revolution in biology will further increase our capacity for positive influence in the evolutionary process. But this does not mean that we should ignore the challenge to interfere with the consequences of our actions or even to deny to nature the right to extirpate. The world's store of genetic material is seen as an inexhaustible source of novel combinations which can be used for the future benefit of man. Each genotype lost before evolution has replaced it is another step in the degradation of our environment. This is an expression of our pragmatic concern with conservation.

The ecologist sees yet another reason for attempting to preserve intact samples of the various biotic communities. The task of extracting the ecological truths is far from complete and new techniques offer constant new opportunities to search more deeply. Lost segments of the ecosystem take with them their unexposed truths. Our opportunity to learn and to understand is permanently impoverished. Strong reasons, therefore, can be advanced for conserving segments of all major communities for the sole purpose of research.

In the other direction, it is being ever more emphatically asked why man should have to seek beauty only in far places. There is creative capacity in man that if given full rein could replace much that is sordid and ugly in our urban environment with beauty, clean air, and green space.

As the history of this age is written, conservation as a concept will be regarded as perhaps the greatest contribution of the New World to human ideas. For the idea had its birth and saw most of its evolution in the United States of America. In a century Powell's vision of sustained yield forestry spread and was adapted to encompass human contact with the entire living world. It gained depth of perception and an almost religious fervor from the Marshes, Muirs, and Thoreaus and scientific rationale from the host of naturalists and ecologists who have emerged from the universities of the Northern Hemisphere. It provided the banner around which rallied all those whose vision of man at his finest involved a sensitive integration into the biophysical world. The Sierra clubs, Audubon societies, wilderness societies, and unions for the conservation of nature have given power to the cause without which the concept could not have found political and physical expression.

But the cause is far from won. At an increasing rate the twin forces of a burgeoning technology and a surging human population are posing ever more difficult problems for the conservators to solve. At an increasing rate we pollute the land, the air, and the sea, convert our rivers into sewers, and spread our indestructible wastes along the remotest shores. An urgent challenge to our ingenuity is the disposal of our wastes.

Over vast areas of the world even the most elementary conservation concepts have still to penetrate. Here fire and destructive agriculture rapidly narrow the gap between man's numbers and his food supply; balanced ecosystems are degraded to uselessness, and biotas vanish forever.

We have not even approached the fascinating but vital problem of man in an enclosed ecosystem. In a very real sense we are denizens of a space capsule to which nothing enters but solar energy. What population of men will the renewable resources of the world support? At what level does the addition of another million people reduce rather than increase the quality of human life? These are questions as close to the core of morality as to conservation. To attack them at all demands the attention of the finest ecological, sociological, and political minds we can muster. The answer is urgent as each passing decade brings us either further on the downgrade or nearer the asymptote. We know not which.

It has been relatively easy to find support for conservation on the American continent where our man-to-space ratio has been low, where hunger has not been an alternative when an acre was allocated to quality of living rather than to food for survival, and where the economic advantages were obvious. The pressures will change as the alternatives gain more immediacy.

Central to conservation on this continent is the gradual change in the legal view of the rights of the individual in relation to the long-term benefits to society. In this context certain recent interpretations of the Supreme Court of the United States of America have the greatest significance. That the individual as a member of a society retains only those liberties specifically allocated to him by the society is an interpretation with broad impact in the natural resources. There still remains in many quarters, however, the narrow interpretation that only consumptive use is really use and should take priority in competition. There is the demand also that even the esthetic qualities of our lives should be justified in dollar values when alternative uses of land are an issue. Conservation lives in both our worlds, the economic and the esthetic; the contribution of the idealogy is equally to both, but the standards of comparison are probably invalid.

It is the unique revelation of man that he not only is consciously sensitive to his own environment but also relates himself to much larger and more complex processes in which he plays a part. His image of the world then becomes an important element in the processes of the world itself.

A central element in our vision of the kind of world we would inhabit is the idealogy of conservation. Within it we find values that we will defend and ideas that we seek to propagate. Man has come full circle from the unwilling participant in the processes of survival to

79

become the only creature whose vision influences those processes. Conservation is the expression of our understanding. It is doubtful if any other idealogy has played so important a part in human affairs and holds so much for man's future.

Even in those unfortunate areas of our own land and others, where avarice and ignorance still triumph, the achievements and ideals of conservation stand as a constant reminder of what could be. Self consciousness once awakened cannot long be ignored.

REFERENCES

1. UDALL, STEWART L., The quiet crisis, 209 pp. New York: Holt, Rinehart, & Winston, 1963.
2. THOMAS, WILLIAM L.; SAUER, CARL O.; BATES, MARSTON; and MUMFORD, LEWIS (eds.), Man's role in changing the face of the earth, xxxviii + 1193 pp. Chicago: University of Chicago Press, 1956.
3. LEOPOLD, A. STARKER; CAIN, S. A.; GABRIELSON, I. N.; COTTAM, CLARENCE; and KIMBALL, T. M., Wildlife management in national parks. Ms. Report to the Secretary of the Interior, U.S.A., 1963.
4. EGLER, FRANK E., Pesticides—in our ecosystem. *Amer. Scientist*, vol. 52, no. 1, pp. 110–136, March 1964.
5. CARSON, RACHEL, Silent spring, 368 pp. Boston: Houghton Mifflin, 1962.
6. HUXLEY, SIR JULIAN S., The human crisis, 88 pp. Seattle: University of Washington Press, 1963.
7. GIBSON, W. C., Lecture manuscript, 1964.
8. OLSON, SIGURD F., A philosophical concept. Proc. First World Conference on National Parks, 1962, pp. 45–50.

G. EVELYN HUTCHINSON

G. Evelyn Hutchinson, Sterling Professor of Zoology at Yale University and world-renowned scientist and writer, is a native of Cambridge, England. He is the son of the late Arthur Hutchinson, professor of mineralogy at Cambridge University and Master of Pembroke College at Cambridge.

After receiving his B.A. and M.A. degrees from Emmanuel College, Cambridge University, and working in Naples and South Africa, Professor Hutchinson joined the Yale faculty in 1928 as an instructor in zoology. He received appointment as Sterling Professor of Zoology in 1945 and served as director of graduate studies in zoology at Yale from 1947 to 1965.

A recipient of many awards, Professor Hutchinson has received an International Education Fellowship, a Guggenheim Fellowship, and the Einar Naumann Medal for outstanding contributions in the field of limnology.

One of Hutchinson's major research interests is a comprehensive study of the lakes of the world. He has studied the inland waters of South Africa and Southwestern Central Asia as well as those of Connecticut, Nevada, and Italy. His work in this field has included studies on the phosphorus and on vitamin cycles in inland waters and on the meaning of the seasonal incidence of the microscopic vegetation of the waters of lakes. He is at present engaged in a cooperative study of the sedimentary record of a number of lakes in various parts of the world. He has also paid much attention to ecological theory.

Professor Hutchinson has authored both popular and scientific works. *The Clear Mirror; A Pattern of Life in Goa and in Indian Tibet* (1936) concerns the Yale University North India Expedition of which he was a member in 1932. His popular works include *The Itinerant Ivory Tower* (1953) and *The Enchanted Voyage and Other Studies* (1962). Hutchinson's love of science is explained by him in *The Itinerant Ivory Tower.* "I am told that part of the material is difficult. I can only reply that I find even the most limited part of the universe very difficult to understand and that it would be a sacrilege to obscure this aspect of the world. I do, however, hope that some readers will see in the book what is so seldom shown in popular expository writing, that contemporary science can be extremely beautiful though often very exasperating, and at times tremendous fun."

Hutchinson's most notable scientific publication is a projected three-volume *Treatise on Limnology*. The first volume was published in 1957, the second is scheduled for publication in 1966, and the third is now in preparation. He has also written some 150 papers and monographs on aquatic insects, limnology, and biogeochemistry.

A member of many honorary societies, including the Elizabethan Club, Royal Entomological Society of London, Linnaean Society of London, American Society of Zoologists, Ecological Society of America, American Philosophical Society, Ecological Society of Great Britain (Hon.), and the National Academy of Sciences, Hutchinson has also held office as president of the Connecticut Academy of Arts and Sciences, the American Society of Limnology and Oceanography, and the International Association for Pure and Applied Limnology.

On Being a Meter
and a Half Long

I AM PARTICULARLY PLEASED to be contributing to the same symposium as Sir Kenneth Clark, known to many readers as the author of, among other books, *Landscape into Art*,[1] because the subject of much of my professional activity has consisted of what may perhaps be called *Landscape into Science*. I would begin by reminding you of what Sir Kenneth says about the Predella of Gentile da Fabriano's *Adoration of the Magi* in the Uffizi, namely, that it has often been noted that here for the first time the sun shone in a picture. This "great gold sun that gardener spring has brought into perfection," in Edith Sitwell's beautiful words,[2] is admittedly stylized. It is shining as the result of the work of an artist who has a great and rather conservative medieval tradition behind him, and it illuminates a landscape, vernal as it may now seem to us, which was the scene, as Huizinga[3] has so clearly demonstrated, of an age of anxiety. At the present time the sun shines much less in pictures. The anxiety that our age feels has been transfused throughout our art. It is only in the works of scientists, who seem wisely or unwisely to be happier, less anxious, and more simple-minded people than do our contemporary writers and artists, that the twentieth century can allow a little sunshine to appear.

I hope that my landscape is sufficiently full of light to be recognizable; it is a landscape with figures some of which we learn to recognize as ourselves. In my remarks about this landscape with figures—plant, animal, or human—I shall emphasize those kinds of study most appropriate to natural-history museums, because a major function of the Smithsonian Institution is to provide a home for the greatest of such museums in the New World.

There are, I think, two rather different ways of looking at nature, which may be termed *extensive* and *intensive*. The greatest investigators doubtless combine both methods, but in any one discovery or group of discoveries we can usually recognize the predominance of one point of view. The final Newtonian triumph of celestial mechanics was an intensive triumph, though not without some extensive background, notably in the then existing body of astronomical observations used by Newton's predecessors. The theory of natural selection of Darwin and Wallace was an extensive vision, though obviously not without intensive elements of theory. The same is probably true of Freud's exploration of the unconscious, which is usually regarded as having produced the third revolution in the intellectual life of the past half millennium. The dichotomy is perhaps basically less a methodological one than a psychological distinction of the kinds of things people like thinking about. The extensive worker prefers sets of examples as subjects for his initial speculations and keeps these or comparable examples in mind throughout. The intensive starts perhaps with a single hint in building a new deductive theory and may not bother to go back to look at nature until many steps later in the mathematical development of the initial intuition.

It is commonly believed that the first steps in any science will be extensive, while the culminating developments will be intensive. Most working investigators probably do not bother very much about this unless they are forced to do so for economic reasons. Many publicists and professional administrators worry very much too much about the matter because they are concerned about making sure that really contemporary developments are considered in their editorials or supported by their institutions. One can easily be told that major academic institutions should support taxonomy only if it is numerical or non-Linnaean or whatever happens at the moment to be the most recent approach. It is considered far more important to be up-to-date than to be interesting and useful. The fact is, however, that except for treatments of the flowering plants, birds, and butterflies of Western Europe and North America, no major area possesses adequate taxonomic treatises on any large group, in which all the significant known complexities are clarified. The production of such works, if done really well, using all modern methods when they are appropriate but not as ends in themselves, would be extremely useful to both pure and applied biologists—a fact that should be sufficient justification for really large-scale support of what is often called old-fashioned. This means, besides adequate institutional aid, which in this country is most fortunately often forthcoming, an active policy of not discouraging people who like such work from doing it. The social and financial pressures that can be put on students and young extensive-minded investigators who might be first-rate taxonomists to become second-rate experimentalists are considerable and in some branches of biology definitely injurious. To a person of the requisite temperament, the construction of a good key to a genus, as readers of Elizabeth Sewell's *Orphic Voice*[4] may suspect, is an activity more clearly allied to the writing of poetry than is any other branch of science. A taxonomic key is in fact a special kind of poem which happens to be of great practical utility. I have heard of people who, knowing little or nothing about plants, have read Bentham and Hooker's *British Flora*[5] for pleasure, just as on a higher level of poetic achievement one can read Shakespeare's sonnets without worrying about the identity of Mr. W. H. or whether the initials may not be, as has recently been suggested, the anagrammatic inversion of those of someone called Harold Wilson.

There is a correlative aspect of taxonomic research which is of some interest in relation to any organization such as the Smithsonian Institution that is directly responsible for collections. From a strictly scientific point of view the results of an investigation constitute a set of propositions, of less or greater generality, that are stated in some more or less formal language. The maintenance of the collection in a museum is, from this point of view, merely something preserved in case more propositions can be based on it. The question arises, however, whether propositions about material objects based on nothing that now materially exists would be in many cases of any great interest. A very good case can be made for the most careful preservation of samples of the things about which we have knowledge, which otherwise might seem remote and unreal. This is true whether or not the object in question has any immediate practical relevance. Dinosaurs and dodos, apes and elephants, all serve to give us a rich time dimension and help us to avoid the all too common triviality of living in the moment as a continuous prelude to rushing thoughtlessly into the future. The whole beauty of nature and of man's work is needed to tell us what the world can be and what there really is to enjoy if we look carefully. The provision of this sort of enjoyment, which is becoming more and more difficult as there are more and more people to be satisfied, needs very careful consideration. A world of boxlike apartment houses provides little that seems marvelous and beautiful. It may be necessary for the majority of people to be engaged in producing and maintaining such a world, but it is also necessary for certain people to make sure that there are an adequate number of emeralds, giraffes, *Welwitschia* plants, birds-of-paradise, *Sequoia* trees, swallowtail butterflies, and giant tortoises, as well as music, painting, and sculpture, to provide the marvelous and the beautiful. This is by no means an insignificant function of the zoological gardens and the national museum. As I have pointed out elsewhere, these activities grade insensibly into those of art galleries.

What I have just been saying is related to an even broader problem that is very seldom considered. I was thinking about part of this address in a botanic garden, founded in the seventeenth century, in which there are a number of rectangular beds set in a lawn, each devoted to a family of flowering plants. Many of these plants were in flower at the time I was there, and the similarity and diversity of the members of each family were obviously apparent and attractive to the eye and the mind. As I was told that certain biologists regarded this display as of little or no educational significance, I began to think about such matters in terms of what was before my eyes. Much of the information set forth in the labeling, grouping, and choice of specimens has been available for two centuries, some of it for much longer. The details of classification and most notably its phylogenetic interpretation have greatly developed in the past century, but what Linnaeus or even Ray wrote can be read comprehendingly today. Much of the information provided by the display in the garden is indeed old-fashioned, in the sense that the propositions embodying it were fashioned some centuries ago. No one denies that if one happens to be interested in the biogenesis of a particular alkaloid it is desirable to have available expert knowledge as to the systematics of the Papaver-aceae so that the right plant for the investigation can be obtained. The question that seems to be raised is whether this sort of information is so esoteric and specialized that it is not worth while implanting it in the minds of students of biology or the general public. In other words, are we living in a world that is inevitably so artificial that the rich diversity of natural objects is an irrelevance of no great educational significance?

Actually the current trend is to go even further, so that the only process that is regarded as of any significance is the obtaining of new information which is stored in libraries or other nonhuman memory stores, from which it can be obtained by taking a book off the shelf or by retrieval from whatever inanimate memory store may be used. Only information acquired in the past five years is often now regarded as significant in some branches of science. The period during which new knowledge retains its bouquet moreover seems to decrease stead-ily, so that if the present attitude persists we might expect the content of science to lose its significance in five months, five minutes, and ultimately five milliseconds or whatever period is needed to get it from recorder to storage unit. In the end no one would know anything except how to keep the apparatus growing, and the learned man would have been automated out of existence. At present he is indeed often condemned to the position of quarryman or miner, encouraged to produce with ever-increasing rapidity more and more information about nature. When a quarry or mine is exhausted the worker must find a new one, if he is young enough. The pleasure of the chase is no doubt great, but it easily becomes obsessive, producing no real satis-faction. This seems to be the situation developing in our universities, the persistent argument between research and teaching being largely an argument as to whether it is more important to get new knowledge or to enjoy the whole form, insofar as we can see it, of what we have. An obsessional attitude to the chase and an obsessional attitude to possession—the attitudes of the hunter or of the miser—are equally inappropriate in their psychopathic form in either learning or teach-ing. Because Ray or Linnaeus loved what they had found out does not mean that we cannot enjoy it; we merely are more fortunate in having more to enjoy.

It is not, however, only with taxonomy, where almost the whole effort is extensive, that I am concerned, but rather with the complete science of landscape with figures, or what is variously called synecology, community ecology, or biocoenology. Here the significant feature is that we are called on to consider the extensive comparative relationships as the subject of intensive study. At the present time this sort of approach is developing a strong evolutionary complexion; in fact at the moment scientific natural history, the proper subject of natural history museums, includes as its central activity what has been called evolutionary ecology.

Since, as I have indicated, we are inevitably among the figures in the landscape and, being roughly 1.5 to 2.0 m. in length, fall into an intermediate size range, though in the larger part of that range, of living organisms, we can only with difficulty get outside the landscape to look at it, and even then we have to allow for the disturbing effect of our activities. The result is that it is rather hard to get a clear idea of the nature of the subject that we are trying to approach. I believe this is the fundamental difficulty in making clear to people outside the field what it is that ecologists actually are trying to do. Perhaps this is best illustrated by a concrete example.

The example that I shall use is the elegant recent work of MacArthur and Levins,[6] who showed, by a simple but quite deep mathematical approach, that given a minimum set of reasonable and very general postulates about possible food habits in competing animal species, two extreme types of evolutionary path are possible. Taking one, the animals tend to develop behavioral mechanisms decreasing the probability of their paths crossing, so emphasizing local ecological allopatry, or alloecism as we may call it; taking the other they tend to develop increasing structural diversity while living in such a way that their paths continually cross, in ecological sympatry or synoecism. In both cases specialization will have occurred allopatrically, but the way in which the species build up communities will be different. Once the theory is developed the dichotomy appears obvious, and once we begin to look for examples, the higher more mobile metazoans provide them in numbers.

A very large amount of work is in fact accumulating that suggests that in most families of insects, in which there are often a number of sympatric species, these species tend to be separated by their choice of specific parts of the biotope in which to live, even though there may be little or no difference in the kind of food resources that are used. In other cases, as in monophagous insects, the behavior will in fact involve a particular choice of food, but, as seems to happen so often in the true sucking bugs of the family Miridae, once the bug is on the right plant it can be either herbivorous or feed on other insects already there. In general, the first case of MacArthur and Levins is likely in small animals in biotopes providing a great deal of mosaic diversity, large enough for each kind of diverse element to be the habitat of one of the species present.

In contrast to this we have in larger more mobile and generally carnivorous animals a marked tendency to synoecism, which is possible only if the species already differ in some way permitting rather different utilization of the varied resources of a habitat in any part of which there is an equal chance of all the species occurring. In general we should expect it in animals whose dimensions are greater than the elements of the mosaic pattern of the habitat, so that as they move about, though the different elements of the mosaic satisfy different needs of the animals, they do not supply specific habitats to different species. Cases, particularly in rather undifferentiated habitats such as the open water of lakes and ponds, can easily be found of structural divergence of allied synoecic animals of very small size, while much larger animals such as rodents and insectivores may show much alloecism, yet on the whole it is reasonable to suppose that the synoecic evolution of communities will mainly occur in rather large animals.

The two extreme kinds of evolution which seem indicated by the MacArthur and Levins[6] approach will have very different paleontological results. In the vertebrates, and most notably in the mammals, sympatric species will probably always be capable of some crossing of paths and as such, if they tend to feed on the same general sort of food, will be subject to evolution by character displacement. At least in mammals what is fossilized is nearly always bone, that is to say the hard structures to which trophic and locomotory muscles are attached. Any adaptive change in movement or feeding is likely to involve skeletal adjustments, either in size or form, or most often in both.

In a great many invertebrates in which the most important differentiae are pleiotropic concomitants of physiological efficiencies in slightly different habitats and of the response mechanisms by which

89

these habitats are found, we may expect to have far less obvious progressive evolution along adaptive lines because the evolution of a specific set of responses, maintaining an organism in a very special optimal habitat, is most unlikely to be recognizable from visible changes in the available fossils.

We thus may, at least in the Metazoa, recognize two modal types of evolutionary change. One is most likely to occur in animals relatively small compared with the mosaic structure of the environment, and involves initially the evolution of mechanisms maintaining the organism in its optimal habitat.

The other is most likely to occur in animals relatively large compared with the mosaic structure of the environment and involves initially the evolution of mechanisms favoring specialized efficient utilization of a particular but not spatially restricted part of the total resources of the habitat.

Often the two types of evolutionary change will be concomitant, but where the first is predominant it will be hard to detect in paleontological material any clear indications of the nature of the adaptations involved, as they are primarily behavioral. In the second type skeletal material should often reflect the adaptation.

Most groups of insects probably exhibit mainly the first type of evolution, most groups of mammals mainly the second. Although in some cases of moderately small animals, such as some carnivorous water bugs, there can be three or perhaps even six sympatric species living synoecically, it is probable that in large mobile animals which provide most of the cases, the synoecic groups will consist only of two or three species per genus. Where more appear, rather subtle alloecic behavioral mechanisms, such as those demonstrated by MacArthur[7] in the American warblers of the genus *Dendroica,* are operating.

In our own species, in which we are large enough to move about over enormous stretches of habitat, it is quite clear that there is no specific part of the terrestrial habitat to which we are limited by innate response mechanisms. At present there is no other species of our family Hominidae living, and so competition with a closely allied species no longer occurs. It is probable from the finds of Leakey that there were a pair of sympatric Hominidae in the early Pleistocene and that these differed in food habits and to some extent in structural differences that were correlated with the difference in food. Even though the MacArthur and Levins dichotomy is not entirely exclusive and not hard and fast where it is applicable, it does at least permit us to recognize in our own nature, in being animals large enough to walk over the ranges of innumerable smaller organisms, large enough to develop an adaptable nervous system independent of inbuilt response mechanisms, and large enough to live more than a season and so have time to learn with our large brain, that we are very different organisms from insects.

Perhaps distinguishing man from insects is not a great feat, but what I want to do is to show that evolutionary processes, even though they all have a basis in natural selection leading to allopatric speciation, are nevertheless of a number, but probably a limited number, of recognizable kinds, of which the kind producing a vast number of insect species is very different from the kind producing ourselves. I want to emphasize this in the present context because it seems to me that evolutionary ecology in conjunction with taxonomy is a most significant activity for a major natural-history museum. The example that I chose led to a very striking if somewhat obvious dichotomy, but other examples of equal human interest could easily be used. The great advantage of a comparative approach, particularly if we are dealing with ourselves, is that it forces us to examine things that are so familiar and obvious that we are apt not to consider their meaning. Instead of comparing large animals and small, we could compare other major kinds of ecological or behavioral categories, diurnal animals with nocturnal, or social with nonsocial, and again find characteristic kinds of evolution. That the right point of view here can lead to the recognition of unsuspected matters of great importance is shown by the beautiful work of Allison Jolly[8] on the differences in the social life of lemurs in Madagascar, which suggest a wealth of new ideas about human evolution. At the present time there is obviously an enormous potential field opening up in evolutionary ecology; we may look forward to the various relevant branches of the Smithsonian Institution producing many "delightful truths," as Sir Thomas Browne would have called them, from this field before a third centennial of James Smithson's birth.

91

REFERENCES

1. CLARK, SIR KENNETH MACKENZIE, Landscape into art, xix + 147 pp. London: J. Murray, 1949.
2. SITWELL, EDITH, The child who saw Midas in Troy Park, 103 pp. London: Duckworth, 1925.
3. HUIZINGA, JOHAN, The waning of the middle ages, viii + 328 pp. Translated by F. Hopman. London: E. Arnold, 1924.
4. SEWELL, ELIZABETH, The orphic voice: poetry and natural history, 463 pp. New Haven: Yale University Press, 1960.
5. BENTHAM, GEORGE, Handbook of the British flora, 6th ed., lxxx + 584 pp. Revised by SIR J. D. Hooker. London: L. Reeve, 1892.
6. MACARTHUR, ROBERT, and LEVINS, RICHARD, Competition, habitat selection, and character displacement in a patchy environment. *Proc. Nat. Acad. Sci.,* vol. 51, no. 6, pp. 1207–1210, June 1964.
7. MACARTHUR, ROBERT H., Population ecology of some warblers of northeastern coniferous forests. *Ecology,* vol. 39, no. 4, pp. 599–619, Oct. 1958.
8. JOLLY, ALLISON, Two social lemurs. Chicago: University of Chicago Press. (In press.)

ARTHUR KOESTLER

Arthur Koestler seems to embody the dilemma of man in the twentieth century in his works, which intensify the moral and social clashes of this age—the ideological and military conflict between totalitarianism and freedom; the struggle between the forces of science and religion, action and thought.

He was born in Budapest on September 5, 1905, and was educated in Vienna. At school he was mostly interested in mathematics, science, and literature. In 1926, after becoming absorbed in the Zionist movement, he left for Palestine, where he worked as a laborer. He then turned to writing, was a foreign correspondent for a few years, and became, at the age of 24, science editor of the Ullstein chain of newspapers of pre-Hitlerite Germany. In this capacity he participated, as the only journalist on board, in the *Graf Zeppelin*'s famous Arctic expedition, and as early as 1930 wrote articles on interplanetary travel and the splitting of the atom.

In 1931 Koestler, who foresaw the Nazi era, joined the Communist Party. In *The God That Failed* (1950) he explains his attraction to Marxism, and in *The Invisible Writing* (1954), the second volume of his autobiography, he describes his seven years in the Communist Party. In 1936, when the Spanish Civil War broke out, he went to Spain as a correspondent for the London *News Chronicle*. He was captured and sentenced to death by the Fascists in 1937, but the British Foreign Office arranged for his release. *Spanish Testament* (1938) and *Dialogue with Death* (1942), a shortened version of the former, cover this period in Spain.

In 1939, while editing the anti-Hitler, anti-Stalin weekly *Zukunft* (Future), he was imprisoned at Le Vernet. That period is the subject of his *Scum of the Earth* (1941). A year later he was again released through British intervention after which he spent time in the British Army and was employed by their Ministry of Information.

Koestler's first novel, *The Gladiators* (1939), has as its subject the revolt of the Roman slaves under Spartacus and expresses his dis-

93

illusionment with the Communist Party. His most widely read political novel, *Darkness at Noon* (1941), which has been translated into thirty languages, is based on the Moscow trials of 1937. Other works of his include *The Lotus and the Robot* (1961), a search for a Far Eastern solution to world problems; *Arrival and Departure* (1943), a novel of a neurotic young Communist who escaped from Nazi torture; *The Yogi and the Commissar* (1945), essays; *Thieves in the Night* (1946), a novel on the Jewish struggle to resettle Palestine in the late thirties; *Promise and Fulfillment* (1949), a history of the Jewish–Arab struggle; *Insight and Outlook* (1949), on science, art, and social ethics; *The Age of Longing* (1951), a novel on the French intelligentsia; *The Trail of the Dinosaur* (1955), warning of the extinction of mankind; *Reflections on Hanging* (1957), which was first syndicated in the London *Observer* and stimulated the movement in England for abolishing the death penalty; *The Sleepwalkers—A History of Man's Changing Vision of the Universe* (1959), which examines the part that man's creative faculty has played in the construction of cosmological systems; and *The Act of Creation* (1964), in which he advanced the theory that all creative activities—the conscious and unconscious processes of scientific discovery, artistic originality, and comic inspiration—have a basic pattern in common that he attempts to define. The doyen of British psychologists, Prof. Sir Cyril Burt, described the book as "a classic contribution to the science of the human mind."

Since World War II Koestler has been a British subject. He lives in London and writes frequently for the *Observer*. He still travels a great deal and has spent time lecturing and writing in the United States. He is a fellow of the Royal Society of Literature, a member of the Institute of Patentees and Inventors, and in 1964–65 was a fellow of the Center for Advanced Studies in the Behavioral Sciences. He disclaims any religious or political attachments at present and in his autobiographical *Arrow in the Blue* (1952) observed: "What I have written may be regarded as the chart of an experimental neurosis produced in the laboratory of our time."

Biological and Mental Evolution—An Exercise in Analogy

ARTHUR KOESTLER

ALLOW ME TO TAKE YOU ON A RIDE on the treacherous wings of analogy, starting with an excursion into genetics. Creativity —the main subject of this paper—is a concept notoriously difficult to define; and it is sometimes useful to approach a difficult subject by way of contrast. The opposite of the creative individual is the pedant, the slave of habit, whose thinking and behavior move in rigid grooves. His biological equivalent is the overspecialized animal. Take, for example, that charming and pathetic creature the koala bear, which specializes in feeding on the leaves of a particular variety of eucalyptus tree and on nothing else; and which, in lieu of fingers, has hooklike claws, ideally suited for clinging to the bark of the tree—and for nothing else. Some of our departments of higher learning seem expressly designed for breeding koala bears.

Julian Huxley has described overspecialization as the principal cause why evolution in all branches of the animal kingdom—except man's—seems to have ended either in stagnation or in extinction. But, having made his point, he drew a conclusion which you may find less convincing. "Evolution," he concluded, "is thus seen as an enormous number of blind alleys, with a very occasional path of progress. It is like a maze in which almost all turnings are wrong turnings."[1] With due respect, I think this metaphor is suspiciously close to the old-fashioned behaviorist's views of the rat in the maze as a paradigm of human learning. In both cases the explicit or tacit assumption is that progress results from a kind of blindman's buff—random mutations preserved by natural selection, or random tries preserved by reinforcement—and that that is all there is to it. However, it is possible to dissent from this view without invoking a *deus ex machina,* or a Socratic daimon, by making the simple assumption that, while random events no doubt play an important part in the picture, that is not all there is to it.

One line of escape from the maze is indicated by a phenomenon known to students of evolution by the ugly name of paedomorphism, a term coined by Garstang[2] some forty years ago. The existence of the phenomenon is well established, but there is little mention of it in the textbooks, perhaps because it runs against the *Zeitgeist;* it indicates that in certain circumstances evolution can retrace its steps, as it were, along the path which led to the dead end and make a fresh start in a more promising direction. To put it simply, paedomorphism means the appearance of some evolutionary novelty in the larval or embryonic stage of the ancestral animal, a novelty which may disappear before the adult stage is reached, but which reappears in the adult descendant. This bit of evolutionary magic is made possible by the well-known mechanism of neoteny, that is to say, the prolongation of bodily development beyond the age of sexual maturity—with the result that breeding takes place while the animal still displays larval or juvenile features. Hardy,[3] de Beer,[4] and others have pointed out that if this tendency toward "prolonged childhood" were accompanied by a corresponding squeezing out of the later adult stages of ontogeny, the result would be a rejuvenation and despecialization of the race which would thus regain some of its lost adaptive plasticity. But of even greater importance than this rewinding of the biological clock is the fact that in the paedomorphic type of evolution selective pressure operates on the early, malleable stages of ontogeny. In contrast to this, gerontomorphism—the appearance of novel characters in the late adult stages—can modify only structures which are already highly specialized. One is accordingly led to expect that the major evolutionary advances were due to paedomorphism and not to gerontomorphism—to changes in the larval or embryonic, and not in the adult, stage.

Let me give an example, which will make clearer what I am driving at. There is now strong evidence in favor of the theory, proposed by Garstang in 1922, that the chordates, and thus we, the vertebrates, descended from the larval stage of some primitive echinoderm, perhaps rather like the sea urchin or sea cucumber. Now an adult sea cucumber would not be a very inspiring ancestor—it is a sluggish creature which looks like an ill-stuffed sausage, lying on the sea bottom. But its free-floating larva is a much more promising proposition: unlike the adult, it has bilateral symmetry, a ciliary band presumed to be the forerunner of the neural fold, and other sophisticated features not found in the adult animal. We must assume that the sedentary adult residing on the sea bottom had to rely on mobile larvae to spread the species far and wide in the ocean, as plants scatter their seeds in the wind; and that the larvae, which had to fend for themselves, exposed to much stronger selective pressures than the adults, gradually became more fishlike; and lastly became sexually mature while still in the free-swimming, larval state—thus giving rise to a new type of animal which never settled on the bottom at all and altogether eliminated the senile, sessile cucumber stage from its life history.

The beauty of the idea strikes one forcibly when one compares a photograph of an adult echinoderm, like the sea urchin, with an adult chordate like the sea squirt. Although it is a mighty step higher up on the evolutionary scale, the adult squirt looks hardly more promising than the urchin, but the difference between the two *larvae* is dramatic; the first looks like a floating jelly, the second is streamlined like a fish.

It seems that the same retracing of steps to escape the dead ends of the maze was repeated at each decisive evolutionary turning point—the last time, so far as we know, when the line which bore our own species branched off from some ancestral primate. It is now generally recognized that the human adult resembles more the embryo of an ape than an adult ape. In both, the ratio of brain weight to body weight is disproportionately high; in both, the closing of the sutures of the skull is retarded to allow for further brain growth. The back to front axis through man's head—the direction of his line of sight—forms an angle of 90° with his spinal column, a condition which in apes and

97

other mammals is found only in the embryonic stage. The same applies to the angle between the urogenital canal and the backbone, which accounts for the singularity of the human way of mating. Other embryonic—or, to use Bolk's[5] term, fetalized—features are the absence of brow ridges, scantness of body hair, retarded development of the teeth, and so on. As Haldane has said, "If human evolution is to continue along the same lines as in the past, it will probably involve a still greater prolongation of childhood and retardation of maturity. Some of the characters distinguishing adult man will be lost."[6] But there is a reverse to the medal, which Aldous Huxley has gleefully shown us: artificial prolongation of the absolute lifespan of man might provide an opportunity for features of the adult ape to reappear in Methuselah. But this only by the way.

The essence of the process which I have described is a *retreat* from highly specialized adult forms of bodily structure and behavior to an earlier, more plastic, and less committed stage—followed by a sudden advance in a new direction. It is as if the stream of life had momentarily reversed its course, flowing uphill for a while, then opened up a new stream bed—leaving the koala bear stranded on its tree like a discarded hypothesis. We have now reached the crucial point in our excursion, because it seems to me that this process of *reculer pour mieux sauter*—of drawing back to leap, of undoing and redoing—is a basic feature of all significant progress, both in biological *and* mental evolution.

It can be shown, I think, that these two types of progress—the emergence of biological novelties and the creation of mental novelties —are analogous processes on different levels of the developmental hierarchy. But to demonstrate the analogy we must proceed stepwise from lower to higher organisms. One of the fundamental properties of living organisms is their power of *self-repair,* and the most dramatic manifestation of this power is the phenomena of regeneration (which Needham called "one of the more spectacular pieces of magic in the repertoire of living organisms"[7]). Primitive creatures, like flatworms, when cut into slices, can regenerate a whole animal from a tiny fragment; amphibians can regenerate limbs and organs; and once more the "magic" is performed by *reculer pour mieux sauter*—by the regression of specialized tissues to a genetically less committed, quasi-embryonic stage, a dedifferentiation or despecialization followed by redifferentiation.

Now the replacement of a lost limb or lost eye is a phenomenon of a quite different order from the adaptive processes in a normal environment. Regeneration could be called a meta-adaptation to traumatizing challenges. The power to perform such meta-adaptations manifests itself only when the challenge exceeds a critical limit and can be met only by having recourse to the genetic plasticity of the embryonic stage. We have just seen that the major phylogenetic changes were brought about by a similar retreat from adult to embryonic forms. Indeed, the main line of development which led up to our species could be described as a series of operations of phylogenetic self-repair: of escapes from blind alleys by the undoing and remolding of maladapted structures.

(Evidently, self-repair by the individual produces no evolutionary novelty; it merely restores the *status quo ante*. But that is all the individual needs in order to regain its normal adaptive balance in a static environment [assuming that the traumatizing disturbance was only a momentary one]. Phylogenetic "self-repair," on the other hand, implies changes in the genotype to restore the adaptive balance in a changing environment.)

As we move toward the higher animals, the power of regenerating physical structures is superseded by the equally remarkable power of the nervous system to reorganize its mode of function. (Ultimately, of course, these reorganizations must also involve structural changes of a fine-grained nature in terms of circuitary, molecular chemistry or both, and so we are still moving along a continuous line.) Lashley[8] taught his rats certain visual discrimination skills; when he removed their optical cortex, the learning was gone, as one would expect; but, contrary to what one would expect, the mutilated rats were able to relearn the same tasks again. Some other brain area, not normally specializing in visual learning, must have taken over this function, deputizing for the lost area.

Similar feats of meta-adaptation have been reported in insects, birds, chimpanzees, and so on. They also occur on the collective level. In a beehive there is normally a fixed division of labor according to age group; each worker specializes in different tasks at different stages of its life. But if all building workers are taken away from the hive, their task is taken over by foragers. The foragers belong to an older age group who were builders earlier on, but lost their wax glands when they entered on their new job. So now they have to grow new wax glands—and they do. Here we have regeneration of structures and reorganization of functions on a heroic scale.

But let us get on to man, and to those lofty forms of self-repair which we call self-realization and which include creativity in its broadest sense. Psychotherapy, ancient and modern, from shamanism down to contemporary forms of abreaction therapy, has always relied on what Ernst Kris[9] has called "regression in the service of the ego." The neurotic with his compulsions, phobias, and elaborate defense mechanisms is a victim of maladaptive specialization—a koala bear hanging on for dear life to a barren telegraph pole. The therapist's aim is to regress the patient to an infantile or primitive condition; to make him retrace his steps to the point where they went wrong, and to come up again, metamorphosed, reborn. Goethe's *Stirb und Werde,* the inexhaustible variations of the archetype of death and resurrection, dark night and spiritual rebirth, all revolve around this basic paradigm —Joseph in the well, Jesus in the tomb, Buddha in the desert, Jonah in the belly of the whale.

There is no sharp dividing line between self-repair and self-realization. All creative activity is a kind of do-it-yourself therapy, an attempt to come to terms with traumatizing experiences. In the scientist's case the trauma is some apparent paradox of nature, some anomaly in the motion of the planets, the sting of data which contradict each other, disrupt an established theory, and make nonsense of his cherished beliefs. In the artist's case, challenge and response are manifested in his tantalizing struggle to express the inexpressible, to conquer the resistance of his medium, to escape from the distortions and restraints imposed by the conventional styles and techniques of his time. In other words, the so-called revolutions in the history of both science and art are successful escapes from blind alleys. The evolution of science is neither continuous nor strictly cumulative except for those periods of consolidation and elaboration which follow immediately after a major breakthrough. Sooner or later, however, the process of consolidation leads to increasing rigidity and orthodoxy, and so into the dead end of overspecialization. The proliferation of esoteric jargons which seems to characterize this phase reminds one sometimes of the monstrous antlers of the Irish elk, and sometimes of the neurotic's elaborate defense mechanisms against the threats of reality. Eventually, the process leads to a crisis, and thus to a new revolutionary breakthrough—followed by another period of consolidation, a new orthodoxy, and so the cycle starts again.

In the history of art, this cyclic process is even more obvious: periods of cumulative progress within a given school and technique end inevitably in stagnation, mannerism, or decadence, until the crisis is resolved by a revolutionary shift in sensibility, emphasis, style.

Every revolution has a constructive and a destructive aspect. In science the destruction is wrought by jettisoning previously unassailable doctrines, including some seemingly self-evident axioms of thought. In art, it involves an equally agonizing reappraisal of accepted values, criteria of relevance, frames of perception. When we discuss the evolution of art and science from the historian's detached point of view, this undoing and redoing process appears as a normal and inevitable part of the whole story. But when we focus our attention on any concrete individual who initiated a revolutionary change, we are immediately made to realize the immense intellectual and emotional obstacles he had to overcome. I mean not only the inertial forces of society; the primary locus of resistance against heretical novelty is inside the skull of the individual who conceives of it. It reverberates in Kepler's agonized cry when he discovered that the planets move in elliptical pathways: "Who am I, Johannes Kepler, to destroy the divine symmetry of the circular orbits!" On a more down-to-earth level the same agony is reflected in Jerome Bruner's[10] experimental subjects who, when shown for a split second a playing card with a *black* queen of hearts, saw it as red, as it should be; and when the card was shown again, reacted with nausea at such a perversion of the laws of nature. To unlearn is more difficult than to learn; and it seems that the task of breaking up rigid cognitive structures and reassembling them into a new synthesis cannot, as a rule, be performed in the full daylight of the conscious, rational mind. It can be done only by reverting to those more fluid, less committed and specialized forms of ideation which normally operate in the twilight below the level of focal awareness. Such intervention of unconscious processes in the creative act is now generally, if sometimes reluctantly, accepted even by behaviorists with a strong positivist bias. Allow me, therefore, to take it for granted that in the period of incubation—to use Graham Wallas's[11] term—the creative individual experiences a temporary regression to patterns of thinking which are normally inhibited in the rational adult.

But it would be a gross oversimplification to identify—as is sometimes done—these patterns with Freud's so-called "Primary Process." The Primary Process is supposedly devoid of logic, governed by the Pleasure Principle, apt to confuse perception and hallucination, expressed in spontaneous action, and accompanied by massive affective discharge. I believe that between this *very* primary process and the so-called secondary process governed by the Reality Principle we must interpolate a whole hierarchy of cognitive structures which are not simply mixtures of primary and secondary processes but are autonomous systems in their own right, each governed by a distinct set of rules. The paranoid delusion, the dream, the daydream, free association, the mentality of children at various ages and of primitives at various stages, should not be lumped together, for each has its own logic or rules of the game. But while clearly different in many respects, all these forms of ideation have certain features in common, since they are ontogenetically, and perhaps phylogenetically, older than those of the civilized adult. I have elsewhere[12] called them "games of the underground," because if not kept under restraint they would play havoc with the routines of disciplined thinking. But under exceptional conditions, when disciplined thinking is at the end of its tether, a temporary indulgence in these underground games may suddenly produce a solution which was beyond the reach of the conscious, rational mind—that new synthesis which Poincaré[13] called the happy combination of ideas, and which I like to call "bisociation" (as distinct from associative routine). I have discussed this process in some detail in a recent book and shall not dwell on its intricate details. The point I want to make here is that the creation of novelty in mental evolution follows the same pattern of *reculer pour mieux sauter,* of a temporary regression to a naive or juvenile level, followed by a forward leap, which we have found in biological evolution. We can carry the analogy further and interpret the Aha reaction, or Eureka cry, as the signal of a happy escape from a blind alley—an act of mental self-repair, achieved by the dedifferentiation of cognitive structures to a more plastic state, and the resulting liberation of creative potentials—the equivalent of the release of genetic growth potentials in regenerating tissues.

It is a truism to say that in mental evolution social inheritance replaces genetic inheritance. But there is a less trivial parallel between phylogenesis and the evolution of ideas: neither of them proceeds along a continuous curve in a strictly cumulative manner. Newton said that if he saw farther than others it was because he stood on the shoulders of giants. But did he really stand on their shoulders or some other part of their anatomy? He adopted Galileo's laws of free fall, but rejected Galileo's astronomy. He adopted Kepler's planetary laws but demolished the rest of the Keplerian edifice. He did not take as his point of departure their completed "adult" theories, but retraced their development to the point where it had gone wrong. Nor was the Keplerian edifice built on top of the Copernican structure. That ramshackle structure of epicycles he tore down and kept only its foundations. Nor did Copernicus continue to build where Ptolemy had left off. He went back two thousand years to Aristarchus. The great revolutionary turns in the evolution of ideas have a decidedly paedomorphic character. The new paradigm, to use Thomas Kuhn's[14] term, which emerges from the revolution is not derived from a previous adult paradigm; not from the aged sea urchin but from its mobile larva, floating in the currents of the ocean. Only in the relatively peaceful periods of consolidation and elaboration do we find gerontomorphism—small improvements to a fully mature body of knowledge. In the history of art the process is again all too obvious; there is no need to elaborate on it.

I began this dissertation with a wistful remark about the treacherous wings of analogy, aware of the fact that those who trust these waxen wings usually share the fate of Icarus. But it is one thing to *argue* from analogy and quite another to point to an apparent similarity which has perhaps not been paid sufficient attention, and then to ask whether that similarity has some significance or whether it is

103

trivial and deceptive. I believe that the parallel between certain processes underlying biological and mental evolution has some significance. Biological evolution could be described as a history of escapes from overspecialization, the evolution of ideas as a series of escapes from the bondage of mental habit. And the escape mechanism in both cases is based on the same principles. We get an inkling of them through the phenomena of regeneration—the remolding of structures and reorganization of functions—which only enter into action when the challenge exceeds a critical limit. They point to the existence of unsuspected, "meta-adaptive" potentials which are inhibited or dormant in the normal routines of existence, and, when revealed, make us sometimes feel that we move like sleepwalkers in a world of untapped resources and unexplored possibilities.

It could be objected that I have presented a reductionist view; that it is sacrilegious to call the creation of a Brahms symphony or of Maxwell's field equations an act of self-repair and to compare it to the mutation of a sea-squirt larva, the regeneration of a newt tail, the relearning process in the rat, or the rehabilitation by patients by psychotherapy. But I think that such a view is the opposite of sacrilegious. It points, however tentatively, at a common denominator, a factor of purposiveness, without invoking a *deus ex machina*. It does not deny that trial and error are inherent in a progressive development. But there is a world of difference between the random tries of the monkey at the typewriter and the process which I called, for lack of a better name, *reculer pour mieux sauter*. The first means reeling off all possible responses in the organism's repertory until the correct one is hit upon by chance and stamped in by reinforcement. The second may still be called trial and error, but of a purposive kind, using more complex, sophisticated methods: a groping and searching, retreating and advancing toward a goal. " 'Purpose,' " to quote Herbert J. Muller,[15] "is not imported into nature, and need not be puzzled over as a strange or divine something . . . It is simply implicit in the fact of organization." This directiveness of vital processes is present all along the line, from conscious behavior down to what Needham called "the striving of the blastula to grow into a chicken." How tenacious and resourceful that striving is has been demonstrated by experimental embryology, from Speeman to Paul Weiss—though its lessons have not yet been fully digested.

Thus to talk of goal-directedness or purpose in ontogeny has become respectable again. In phylogeny the monkey still seems to be hammering away at the typewriter, perhaps because the crude alternatives that had been offered—amorphous entelechies, or the Lysenko brand of Lamarckism—were even more repellent to the scientific mind. On the other hand, some evolutionary geneticists are beginning to discover that the typewriter is structured and organized in such a way as to defeat the monkey, because it will print only meaningful words and sentences. In recent years the rigid, atomistic concepts of Mendelian genetics have undergone a softening process and have been supplemented by a whole series of new terms with an almost holistic ring. Thus we learn that the genetic system represents a "microhierarchy" which exercises its selective and regulative control on the molecular, chromosomal, and cellular level; that development is "canalized," stabilized by "developmental homeostasis" or "evolutionary homeostasis"[16] so that mutations affect not a single unit character but a "whole organ in a harmonious way"[17]; and finally that these various forms of "internal selection" create a restricted "mutation spectrum"[18] or may even have a "direct, molding influence guiding evolutionary change along certain avenues"[19]—and all this happens long before external, Darwinian selection gets to work. But if this is the case, then the part played by a lucky chance mutation is reduced to that of the trigger which releases the coordinated action of the system; and to maintain that evolution is the product of blind chance means to confuse the simple action of the trigger, governed by the laws of statistics, with the complex, purposive processes which it sets off. Their purposiveness is manifested in different ways on different levels of the hierarchy, from the self-regulating properties of the genetic system through internal and external selection, culminating perhaps in the phenomena of phylogenetic self-repair: escapes from blind alleys and departures in new directions. On each level there is trial and error, but on each level it takes a more sophisticated form. Some thirty years ago Tolman and Krechevsky[20] created a stir by proclaiming that the rat learns to run a maze by forming hypotheses; soon it may be permissible to extend the metaphor and to say that evolution progresses by making and discarding hypotheses.

Any directive process, whether you call it selective, adaptive, or expectative, implies a reference to the future. The equifinality of

105

developmental processes, the striving of the blastula to grow into an embryo, regardless of the obstacles and hazards to which it is exposed, might lead the unprejudiced observer to the conclusion that the pull of the future is as real and sometimes more important than the pressure of the past. The pressure may be compared to the action of a compressed spring, the pull to that of an extended spring, threaded on the axis of time. Neither of them is more or less mechanistic than the other. If the future is completely determined in the Laplacian sense, then there is nothing to choose between the actions of the two springs. If it is indeterminate in the Heisenbergian sense, then indeterminacy works in both directions, and the distant past is as blurred and unknowable as the future. And if there is something like a free choice operating within the air bubbles in the stream of causality, then it must be directed toward the future and oriented by feedback from the past.

REFERENCES

1. HUXLEY, JULIAN, Man in the modern world, 191 pp. New York: Mentor Books, 1948.
2. GARSTANG, WALTER, The theory of recapitulation: a critical re-statement of the biogenetic law. *Journ. Linnean Soc. London, Zoology,* vol. 35, no. 232, pp. 81–101, Sept. 30, 1922.
3. HARDY, A. C., Escape from specialization, pp. 122–42 *in* Evolution as a process, Julian Huxley, A. C. Hardy, and E. B. Ford (eds.). London: Allen & Unwin, 1954.
4. DE BEER, G. R., Embryos and ancestors, x, 108 pp. Oxford: Clarendon Press, 1940.
5. BOLK, LOUIS, Das Problem der Menschwerdung. Jena: Gustav Fisher, 1926.
6. HALDANE, J. B. S., The causes of evolution, 235 pp. London: Longmans, Green, 1932, p. 150.
7. NEEDHAM, A. E., How living organisms repair themselves. *New Scientist,* vol. 12, no. 259, pp. 284–287, Nov. 2, 1961.
8. LASHLEY, KARL SPENCER, Brain mechanisms and intelligence, xiv, 186 pp. Chicago: University of Chicago Press, 1929.
9. KRIS, ERNST, Psychoanalytic explorations in art, 358 pp. New York: International Universities Press, 1952.
10. BRUNER, J. S., and POSTMAN, L., On the perception of incongruity: a paradigm. *Journ. Personality,* vol. 18, pp. 206–223, 1949.
11. WALLAS, GRAHAM, The art of thought, x, 129 pp. London: C. A. Watts, 1945.
12. KOESTLER, ARTHUR, The act of creation, 751 pp. New York: Macmillan, 1964.
13. POINCARÉ, H., Mathematical creation, pp. 22–32 *in* The creative process, B. Ghiselin (ed.). Berkeley: University of California Press, 1952.
14. KUHN, THOMAS S., The structure of scientific revolutions, xv, 172 pp. Chicago: University of Chicago Press, 1962.
15. MULLER, HERBERT J., Science and criticism, 303 pp. New Haven: Yale University Press, 1943.

16. CANNON, HERBERT GRAHAM, The evolution of living things, ix, 180 pp. Manchester: Manchester University Press, 1958.
17. WADDINGTON, C. H., How do adaptations occur? *The Listener,* vol. 48, no. 1237, pp. 805–06, Nov. 13, 1952.
18. SPURWAY, H., Remarks on Vavilov's law of homologous variation, *in* Supplemento: La ricerca scientifica (Pallanza symposium) 18. Rome: Consiglio Naz. Ricerche, 1949.
19. WHYTE, LANCELOT LAW, Internal factors in evolution, 128 pp. New York: G. Braziller, 1965.
20. KRECHEVSKY, I., "Hypotheses" in rats. *Psychological Rev.,* vol. 39, no. 6, pp. 516–532, 1932.

CLAUDE LÉVI-STRAUSS

Claude Lévi-Strauss, eminent anthropologist and ethnologist, was born in 1908 in Brussels, Belgium. After receiving his "Agregation" in Paris, he taught sociology at the University of São Paulo in Brazil. He was also a visiting professor at the New School for Social Research in New York from 1941 to 1944, having fled occupied France.

Two years later he was in Washington, D.C., serving as cultural attaché for the French Embassy, a post he held until 1947. In 1948 he returned to France, as associate curator of the *Musée de l'Homme,* Paris. He is now a professor at the *Collège de France* and a director of studies at the *École pratique des hautes études,* Paris.

Lévi-Strauss has done field work in southern and central Mato Grosso, Brazil (1935–36), and in northern and western Mato Grosso and southern Amazonas, Brazil (1938 and 1939).

Possessing a thorough knowledge of and high respect for American anthropology, he cites and incorporates it in his own work, along with French and British anthropology, thereby exerting a unifying and internationalizing influence on the field. His interests are wide, encompassing philosophy, zoology, and literature. In Rodney Needham's *Structure and Sentiment* the author states: "I am convinced that *Les Structures élémentaires de la Parenté* is a masterpiece, a sociological classic of the first rank. . . . Lévi-Strauss's work is part of the continuing application, in the study of human society, of ideas and methodological rules worked out in the end of the last century and the beginning of this by the French sociological school. This school is the source of nearly everything that is best in social anthropology . . ."

Lévi-Strauss has done much work on the structural analysis of kinship, symbolism and symbolic thought, and the analysis of anthropology. Claire Jacobson wrote, in her translator's preface to his *Structural Anthropology* (1958): "For the past decade and a half Claude Lévi-Strauss has been the most influental anthro- pological theorist in France. . . . Lévi-Strauss is primarily concerned with universal, that is, basic social and mental processes of which cultural institutions are the concrete external projections or manifestations. . . . Lévi-Strauss has long been one of the chief exponents of the structural method; he considers the relations among phenomena, rather than the nature of the phenomena themselves, and the systems into which these relations enter. . . . Lévi-Strauss's anthropology emphasizes the close relationship between field work and theory, between the description of social phenomena and structural analysis, as two phases of the same process. . . . He is concerned with relating . . . the physiological to the psychological, the objective analysis of institutions to the subjective experience of individuals."

M. Lévi-Strauss has also written many other articles and books both in French and English, such as his contributions to the Smithsonian's "Handbook of South American Indians" (Bureau of American Ethnology Bulletin 143, 1946–1959), *Race and History* (1952), *Tristes Tropiques* (1955), *Totemism* (1962), *La Pensée Sauvage* (1962), and *Le Cru et le Cuit* (1964).

M. Lévi-Strauss liked the following statement of Jean Pouillon's from the 1956 edition of *Les Tempes Modernes* because he modestly hoped it did typify him: "Lévi-Strauss is certainly not the first nor the only one to have emphasized the structural character of social phenomena, but his originality consists in taking that character seriously and in serenely deriving all the consequences from it."

Anthropology:
Its Achievements and Future

CLAUDE LÉVI-STRAUSS

AMONG THE MANY CHERISHED RECOLLECTIONS that I have retained of the years I spent in the United States, one remains outstanding because it is associated with what, owing to my inexperience, appeared to me as something of a discovery. Indeed, it embodies for me to this day the unfathomable wealth and mystery of the city of New York.

This apparent discovery took place quite casually, one day, on lower Broadway, when I stumbled upon a bookstore which specialized in secondhand government publications and where could be bought, for two or three dollars apiece, most of the *Annual Reports* of the Bureau of American Ethnology.

I can hardly describe my emotion at this find. That these sacrosanct volumes, in their original green and gold bindings, representing most of what will remain known about the American Indian, could actually be bought and privately owned was something I had never dreamed of. To my mind, they belonged rather to the same irredeemable past as the beliefs and customs of which they spoke. It was as though the civilization of the American Indian had suddenly come alive through the physical contact that these contemporary books established between me and their time. I felt somewhat akin to a sixteenth-century scholar who, finding in what must have corresponded to our secondhand bookstores, old manuscript copies of the works of Homer, Plato, or Vergil, is struck by the evidence that these great men had actually existed since someone had seen and transcribed their written word.

Although my financial resources were more than scant and three dollars represented all I had to spend on food for the same number of days, this sum seemed negligible when it could pay for one of these marvelous publications, more alluring to the eye than any costly art books, such as Mallery's *Pictographs of North American Indians,*[1] Matthews's *Mountain Chant,*[2] Fewkes's *Hopi Katcinas,*[3] or such treasure troves of knowledge as Stevenson's *Zuñi Indians,*[4] Boas's *Tsimshian Mythology,*[5] Roth's works on the Guiana Indians,[6, 7] and Curtin and Hewitt's *Seneca Fiction, Legends, and Myths.*[8]

Thus it happened that with volume after volume and at the cost of some privations I built up an almost complete set (there is still one volume missing) of the *Annual Reports,* 1 to 48, which belong to the "great period" of the Bureau of American Ethnology. At that time, I was far from imagining that a few months later I would be invited by the Bureau to become a contributor to one of its major undertakings: the seven-volume *Handbook of South American Indians.*[9]

Notwithstanding this close association and the years that have since elapsed, the work of the Bureau of American Ethnology has lost for me none of its glamor, and I still feel toward it an admiration and respect which are shared by innumerable scholars the world over. Since it so happens that in the same year that marks the 200th anniversary of James Smithson the life of the Bureau has come to an end (though its activities are carried on under a new guise), the time may be fitting to pay tribute both to the memory of the founder of the Smithsonian Institution and to the Bureau which has been one of its greatest achievements and certainly a unique one of its kind.

Ever since it was founded in 1879 (which, incidentally, meant the emancipation of ethnology from geography and geology wherewith it had been merged so far), not only did the Bureau avail itself fully of the amazing opportunity provided by the presence of scores of native tribes at a few hours' or days' travel from the great cities, but also, as a distinguished anthropologist Dr. Godfrey Lienhardt puts it in a recent book: "The accounts of custom and culture published by the Bureau compare in thoroughness and quality of reporting with modern ethnographic studies."[10] We are thus primarily indebted to the Bureau for instituting standards of scholarship that still guide us, even though we but rarely succeed in attaining them.

112

Above all, the collection of native texts and factual observations contained in the forty-eight major *Reports* and certain of the subsequent ones, in the two hundred *Bulletins,* and in the *Miscellaneous Publications* is so impressive that, despite the use they have been put to for nearly a century, it is safe to say that only the surface has been scratched. This being the case, one can only wonder at the neglect into which this invaluable material has temporarily fallen; as if the far less rich material with which we must content ourselves concerning the beliefs and customs of Greece and Rome were not still laden with as yet unexploited and occasionally unnoted data! The day will come when the last primitive culture will have disappeared from the earth, compelling us to realize only too late that the fundamentals of mankind are irretrievably lost. Then, and for centuries to come, as happened in the case of our own ancestral civilizations, hosts of scholars will devote themselves to reading, analyzing, and commenting on the publications of the Bureau of American Ethnology which preserve so much more than has been preserved of other bygone cultures (not to mention the unpublished manuscripts placed in the Bureau's custody). And if ever we succeed in enlarging our narrow-minded humanism to make it include each and every expression of human nature, thereby perhaps ensuring to mankind a more harmonious future, it is to undertakings such as those of the Bureau of American Ethnology that we shall owe it.

However, nothing could be farther from my mind than the notion that the work of the Bureau belongs to the past; I believe, on the contrary, that all of us, together with its legal successor the Smithsonian Office of Anthropology, should seek in these achievements a living inspiration for the scientific task ahead of us.

It has become the fashion in certain circles to speak of anthropology as a science on the wane, on account of the rapid disappearance of its traditional subject matter: the so-called primitives. Or else it is claimed that in order to survive anthropology should abandon fundamental research and become an applied science, dealing with the problems of developing countries and pathological aspects of our own society. I should not want to minimize the obvious interest of these new researches, but I feel nevertheless that there is, and will remain for a long time to come, much to be done along the more traditional

113

lines. It is precisely because the so-called primitive peoples are becoming extinct that now, more than ever, their study should be given absolute priority.

And it is not too late for hundreds of anthropologists to set to work. As early as 1908, almost sixty years ago, Sir James Frazer, in his inaugural lecture at Liverpool University, stated that classical anthropology was nearing its end. What have we witnessed instead? Two great wars together with scientific development have shaken the world and destroyed physically or morally a great many native cultures. But this process, however disastrous, has not been entirely one way. The first World War gave rise indirectly to Malinowski's new anthropology by obliging him to share the life of the Trobriand Islanders in a more durable and intimate manner than, perhaps, he would have done otherwise. And as a consequence of the second World War, anthropologists were given access to a new world: the New Guinea highlands, with a population of 600,000 to 800,000 souls whose specific institutions are changing presently our traditional outlook on many theoretical problems. Likewise, the establishment of the new Federal Capital of Brazil and the building of roads and aerodromes in remote parts of South America have led to the discovery of small tribes in areas where no native life was thought to exist.

Of course, these opportunities will be the last, and there is no future ahead. Moreover, the compensation they afford is small indeed, compared with the high rate of extinction afflicting primitive tribes the world over. There are about 40,000 natives left in Australia as opposed to 250,000 at the beginning of the nineteenth century, most, if not all of them, hunger-stricken and disease-ridden, threatened in their deserts by mining plants, atom bomb test grounds and missile ranges. Between 1900 and 1950 over ninety tribes were wiped out in Brazil where instead of a hundred, there are now barely thirty still living in a state of relative isolation. During the same period, fifteen South American languages have ceased to be spoken. Scores of similar examples could be given.

Yet this is no reason to become discouraged. It is undoubtedly true that we have less and less material to work with. But anthropological methods and procedures having made considerable progress in the meantime, we are able to compensate to some extent for this diminishing volume by putting it to better use, thanks to our greater theoretical and factual knowledge and more refined techniques of observation. If I may put it that way, we have not much left to work with, but we will manage to "make it last." We have learned how to look for the cultural "niches" in which traditional lore finds refuge and where it offers the strongest resistance to the impact of civilization: language, kinship, ethnobotany, ethnozoology, and the like.

But although the physical disappearance of populations that remained faithful till the very end to their traditional way of life does, indeed, constitute a threat to anthropology, curiously enough a more immediate one comes from an evolution that has been taking place in such parts of the world as Asia, Africa, and the American Andes, which used to be considered as falling also within the realm of anthropological studies. The demography of these regions was always high and it shows no sign of decreasing; quite the contrary; physically speaking, the subject matter is still there, as rich as ever, if not richer still. This new threat to our studies is not then so much of a quantitative as of a qualitative nature, and this proves to be doubly true: in the first place, these large populations are changing fast, and their culture is resembling more and more that of the Western world. Like the latter, it tends to fall outside the field of anthropology. But this is not all, for the mere fact of being subjected to ethnographical investigation seems distasteful to these peoples, as though by studying the ways in which their old beliefs and customs differed from our own, we were granting these differences an absolute status and conferring upon them a more enduring quality.

Contemporary anthropology thus finds itself in a paradoxical situation. For it is out of a deep feeling of respect toward cultures other than our own that the doctrine of cultural relativism was evolved; and it now appears that this doctrine is deemed unacceptable by the very peoples on whose behalf it was upheld, while those ethnologists who favor unilinear evolutionism find unexpected support from peoples who desire nothing more than to share in the benefits of industrialization and prefer to look at themselves as temporarily backward rather than permanently different.

Hence the distrust in which traditional anthropology is held nowadays in some parts of Africa and Asia. Economists and sociologists

115

are welcome, while anthropologists are tolerated at best, and from certain areas they are simply banned. Why perpetuate even in writing old usages and customs which are doomed to die? The less consideration and attention they receive, the faster they will disappear. And even should they not disappear, it is better not to mention them, lest the outside world realize that one's culture is not as fully abreast with modern civilizations as one deludes oneself into believing it to be. There have been periods in our own history when we too have yielded to the same delusion, only to find ourselves struggling to regain balance after eradicating so recklessly the roots that held us back to our past. Let us hope that this dire lesson will not be lost on others.

The question is, in effect: What can we do to keep it from being lost? Is there a way of making peoples realize that they have a tremendous responsibility toward themselves and toward mankind as a whole, which is not to let perish before it has been fully recorded this past it is their unprecedented privilege to experience on a par with their incipient future? The suggestion has been made that in order to render anthropology less distasteful to its former human raw material, it will suffice to reverse the roles and occasionally allow ourselves to be "ethnographized" by those for whom we were once solely the ethnographers. In this way, each in turn will get the upper hand. And since there will be no permanent privilege, nobody will have grounds to feel inferior to anybody else. At the same time, we shall get to know more about ourselves through the eyes of others and human knowledge in general will derive an ever-growing profit from this reciprocity of perspective.

Well meant as it undoubtedly is, this solution appears to me naive and unworkable; as though the problems involved in the great confrontation now taking place between Western culture and the rest of the world were as simple and superficial as those of children unaccustomed to play together, whose quarrels can be settled by making them follow the elementary rule: "Let me play with your dolls and I shall let you play with mine." To arrive at an understanding between people who are not merely estranged from one another by their physical appearance and their peculiar ways of life, but also stand on an unequal footing to one another, is a different problem altogether.

Anthropology is not a dispassionate science like astronomy, which springs from the contemplation of things at a distance. It is the outcome of a historical process which has made the larger part of mankind subservient to the other, and during which millions of innocent human beings have had their resources plundered, their institutions and beliefs destroyed, while they themselves were ruthlessly killed, thrown into bondage, and contaminated by diseases they were unable to resist. Anthropology is daughter to this era of violence: its capacity to assess more objectively the facts pertaining to the human condition reflects, on the epistemological level, a state of affairs in which one part of mankind treated the other as an object.

A situation of this kind cannot be soon forgotten, even less erased. It is not on account of its mental endowments that only the Western world has given birth to anthropology, but rather as a consequence of the fact that exotic cultures, treated by us as mere things, could be studied, accordingly, as things. We did not feel concerned by them whereas we cannot help their feeling concerned by us. Between our attitude toward them and their attitude toward us there is and can be no parity.

Therefore, if native cultures are ever to look at anthropology as a legitimate pursuit, and not as a sequel to the colonial era or that of economic domination, it cannot suffice for the players simply to change camps while the anthropological game remains the same. Anthropology itself must undergo a deep transformation in order to carry on its work among those cultures whose study it was intended for because they lacked a written record of their past history. This, however, it will achieve in an altogether different way, since instead of making up for this gap through the application of special methods, the aim will be to fill it in. Whenever practiced by members of the culture which it endeavors to study, anthropology loses its specific nature and becomes rather akin to archeology, history, and philology. For inasmuch as anthropology is the science of culture as seen from the outside, it follows that the first concern of people made aware of their independent existence and of their originality could not be to observe from the outside the culture of their former masters while allowing the latter to observe their own culture also from the outside, but to claim the right to observe this culture of theirs themselves, and in the only way, that is, from the inside. The obvious conclusion is that anthro-

117

pology will survive in a changing world by allowing itself to perish in order to be born again under a new guise.

Anthropology is thus confronted with two tasks which would prove contradictory only were they to be undertaken simultaneously in the same field. Wherever native cultures, though disappearing physically, have remained to some extent morally intact, anthropological research should be carried out along traditional lines, and the means at its disposal increased to the utmost. And wherever the opposite situation prevails, that is, where populations have remained physically strong while their culture is rapidly veering toward our own, anthropology should shift its goals and, while being taken over progressively by scholars from the land, adopt aims and methods similar to those which, from the Renaissance on, have proved fruitful for the study of our own culture.

From the very beginning, the Bureau of American Ethnology has had to face this twofold necessity by reason of the peculiar situation of the American Indian who allied cultural remoteness and physical proximity, together with a tremendous will to live, at least among some tribes, despite all the ordeals they have been subjected to; thus the Bureau was compelled from the start to act both ways: on the one hand, by conducting ethnographical surveys, the precision and rigor of which have set up a standard that cannot be surpassed, and on the other by encouraging the natives themselves to become their own linguists, philologists, and historians. If the cultural riches of Africa, Asia, and Oceania are to be saved, it will only be on the condition that, following this example, we succeed in raising dozens (and they themselves hundreds) of such men as Francis La Flesche, son of an Omaha chief, James Murie, a Skidi Pawnee, George Hunt, a Kwakiutl, and many others, some of whom, like La Flesche and Murie, were on the staff of the Bureau. When we consider that this was taking place more than fifty years ago, we can but marvel at such maturity and foresight and hope for the extension, on a world scale, of what a handful of resolute and enlightened men and women knew should be done in the wide field of American studies. And indeed, they did it in such an efficient way that through less than a century of effort on their part a great deal more has been preserved of the native cultures of North America than all we know of Egypt, Greece, or Rome.

This does not mean that we should be content merely to add similar material to that which is already available. There remains to be saved such a considerable amount that the urgency of the task risks well making us overlook the present evolution of anthropology which as it increases in quantity is also changing in quality. Recognition of this fact should make us more confident in the future of our studies, and it can be verified in many ways. To begin with, new problems have arisen which can still be solved, even though they have received but scant attention thus far. It is worth noting, for instance, with what disdain until recently anthropologists have neglected to study the relationship, in the case of each crop, between the amount of work involved and the yield, as well as the latter's elasticity. Yet one of the keys to the understanding of the social and religious importance of yams, which is so striking throughout Melanesia, can probably be found in the remarkable elasticity of the yield. The farmer who is exposed to harvesting far less than he actually needs must plant far more in order to be reasonably certain to have enough. Conversely, if the harvest is plentiful it can so widely exceed expectations that to consume it all becomes impossible; this leaves no other use for it than competitive display and social food presentation. In cases such as the above, as in many others, we must learn to translate, in terms of several different codes, phenomena that we have been apprehending so far in terms of one or two codes only and thus render the observed phenomena a great deal more significant.

A wide system of equivalents could then be established between the truths of anthropology and those of neighboring sciences which have been progressing at a similar pace. I am thinking not only of economics, but of biology, demography, sociology, psychology, and logics, for it is through a number of such adjustments that the originality of our field will best appear.

There has been much question lately as to whether anthropology belonged among the humanities or among the natural sciences. In my opinion this is a false problem, since anthropology has the unique feature of not lending itself to such a distinction. It has the same subject matter as history, but for lack of time perspective it cannot use the same methods. Its own methods tend rather toward those of sciences not devoted to the study of man, though synchronically oriented like anthropology itself. As in every other scientific under-taking, these methods aim at discovering invariant properties beneath the apparent particularity and diversity of the observed phenomena.

Will this assignment deter anthropology from a humanistic and historical outlook? Quite the opposite is true. Of all the branches of our discipline, physical anthropology is probably the closest to the natural sciences. For this very reason, it is worth noting that by refining its methods and techniques it has been getting ever closer to, not farther from, a humanistic outlook.

For the physical anthropologist to look for invariant properties traditionally meant to look for factors devoid of adaptive value and from the presence or absence of which something could be learned about the racial divisions of mankind. Our colleagues are less and less convinced, though, that any such factors really do exist. The sickle-cell gene, formerly held as one, can no longer be considered in that light if, as is now generally accepted, it carries a certain measure of immunity to malaria. However, as Dr. Frank B. Livingstone[11] has brilliantly demonstrated, what appears as an irretrievable loss from the point of view of long-range, conjectural history can be viewed as a definite gain from that of history as historians conceive it, that is, both concrete and at close range. For by reason of the adaptative value of the sickle-cell gene, a map showing its distribution throughout the African continent would make it possible for us to read, as it were, African history in the making, and the knowledge thus obtained could be correlated with that acquired from language and other cultural maps. Therefore, the same invariant properties which have vanished at the superficial level where they were sought for originally reappear at a deeper functional level; and wheras they seem to grow less informative, they turn out to be more meaningful.

This remarkable process is actually taking place everywhere in our field. Dr. George M. Foster[12] has recently given new life to what most of us held to be an exhausted question: the origin of the potter's wheel. This he achieved by pointing out that an invention is neither simply a new mechanical device nor a material object that can be described objectively, but rather a manner of proceeding which may avail itself of a number of different devices, some of them crude and others more elaborate. In the field of social organization, I myself have tried to show that kinship systems should not be described by their external features such as the number of terms they use, or the way they classify, merge, and distinguish all possible ties between individuals. In so doing, all we can hope to obtain is a long list of types and subtypes which are there simply as meaningless objects, while if we try to find out how they work, that is, what kind of solidarity they help to establish within the group, their apparent multiplicity finds itself reduced to a few basic and meaningful principles.

Similarly, in the field of religion and mythology, an attempt to reach beyond external features, which can only be described and arbitrarily classified by each scholar according to preconceived ideas, shows that the bewildering diversity of mythical motifs can be reduced to a very few number of schemes, each of which appears endowed with a specific operational value. At the same time there emerge for each culture certain sets of transformation rules which make it possible to include in the same group myths previously held to be markedly different.

These few examples, chosen among many others, tend to show that anthropology's traditional problems are assuming new forms while none of them can be said to be exhausted. The distinctive feature of anthropology, and that which singles it out among other human sciences, is to look at man from the very point where, at each period of history, it was considered that anything manlike had ceased to exist. During Antiquity and the Middle Ages this point was set up too close for making observation possible, since each culture or society was inclined to locate it on their neighbor's doorstep. And within a century or so, when the last native culture will have disappeared from the earth and our only interlocutor will be the electronic computer, it will have become so remote that we may well doubt whether the same kind of approach will deserve to be called "anthropology" any longer. Between these limits lies the only chance that man ever had or will have to look at himself in the flesh while still remaining a problem unto himself, though one he knows can be solved since it is already certain that the outer differences conceal a basic unity.

Let us suppose for a moment that astronomers should warn us that an unknown planet was nearing the earth and would remain for twenty or thirty years at close range, afterward to disappear forever.

121

In order to avail ourselves of this unique opportunity, neither effort nor money would be spared to build telescopes and satellites especially designed for the purpose. Should not the same be done at a time when one-half of mankind, only recently acknowledged as such, is still so near to the other half that except for men and money its study raises no problem, although it will soon become impossible forever? If the future of anthropology could be seen in this light, no study would appear more urgent and no other could compete with it in importance. For native cultures are disintegrating faster than radioactive bodies, and the Moon, Mars, and Venus will still be at the same distance from the Earth when that mirror which other civilizations still hold up to us will have so receded from our eyes that however costly and elaborate the instruments at our disposal we may never again be able to recognize and study this image of ourselves which will be lost and gone forever.

REFERENCES

1. MALLERY, GARRICK, Pictographs of the North American Indians, pp. 3–256. 4th Ann. Rep. (1882–83) Bur. Ethnol., 1886.
2. MATTHEWS, WASHINGTON, The mountain chant: a Navajo ceremony, pp. 379–467. 5th Ann. Rep. (1883–84) Bur. Ethnol., 1887.
3. FEWKES, JESSE WALTER, Hopi katcinas, pp. 3–126. 21st Ann. Rep. (1899–1900) Bur. Amer. Ethnol., 1903.
4. STEVENSON, MATILDA COXE. The Zuñi Indians, pp. 1–634. 23d Ann. Rep. (1901–02) Bur. Amer. Ethnol., 1904.
5. BOAS, FRANZ, Tsimshian mythology, pp. 29–1037. 31st Ann. Rep. (1909–10) Bur. Amer. Ethnol., 1916.
6. ROTH, WALTER E., An inquiry into the animism and folk-lore of the Guiana Indians, pp. 103–386. 30th Ann. Rep. (1908–09) Bur. Amer. Ethnol., 1915.
7. ———, An introductory study of the arts, crafts, and customs of the Guiana Indians, pp. 25–745. 38th Ann. Rep. (1916–17) Bur. Amer. Ethnol., 1924.
8. CURTIN, JEREMIAH, and HEWITT, J. N. B., Seneca fiction, legends, and myths, pp. 37–814. 32d Ann. Rep. (1910–11) Bur. Amer. Ethnol., 1918.
9. STEWART, JULIAN H. (ed.), Handbook of South American Indians. Bur. Amer. Ethnol. Bull. 143, 7 vols., 1946–1959.
10. LIENHARDT, GODFREY, Social anthropology, x, 216 pp. New York: Oxford University Press, 1964, p. 24.
11. LIVINGSTONE, FRANK B., Anthropological implications of sickle cell gene distribution in West Africa. *Amer. Anthropologist,* vol. 60, no. 3, pp. 533–62, June 1958.
12. FOSTER, GEORGE M., The potter's wheel: an analysis of idea and artifact in invention. *Southwestern Journ. Anthrop.,* vol. 15, no. 2, pp. 99–119, 1959.

LEWIS MUMFORD

In an earlier age, Lewis Mumford would have been called a philosopher; but since philosophers are now specialists in logic or semantics, he prefers to call himself a generalist, or in the terms Carlyle comically applied to the hero of *Sartor Resartus,* a *"Professor der allerley Wissenschaft."*

Mumford was born in Flushing, L.I., on October 19, 1895, and until past forty was a resident of New York. As a young experimenter in radio, he went to a technical high school (Stuyvesant) with the intention of becoming an electrical engineer, but his nearest approach to that was to get further training as a radio electrician in the United States Navy in 1918. Between 1912 and 1919 he studied mainly at City College, with further work at Columbia University and the New School for Social Research. Though he received no degree of any kind till he accepted an LL.D. from the University of Edinburgh in 1965, as a university teacher he has always held the rank of full professor. Among other institutions he has served at Stanford University, as professor of humanities, 1942–44; at the University of Pennsylvania, as professor of city and regional planning, 1951–61; and Visiting Bemis Professor at the Massachusetts Institute of Technology, 1957–60.

Apart from his writing, Mumford was a co-founder and active member of the Regional Planning Association of America, which in the twenties laid the foundations for a broad policy of housing, community-building, and urban development on a regional scale—a work that is beginning only now to bear fruit. He served as a member of the Board of Higher Education of New York City (1935–1937) in the active reorganization of the municipal colleges, while later he served on the Commission on Teacher Education of the American Council on Education. As an upholder of the American tradition of democracy, which his own work as cultural interpreter of America's buried past had helped to renew, he became an active opponent of totalitarianism in every form, and from 1935 on he exerted himself to prepare the country for armed resistance to

Nazi Germany, writing a "Call to Arms" in the *New Republic* in May 1938, four months before the betrayal at Munich, and following this with *Men Must Act* (1939) and *Faith for Living* (1940). When the war was over he continued this campaign in an effort to awaken attention to the new form of totalitarianism effected through nuclear weaponry. One of his early articles, "The Social Effects of the Atom Bomb," which was required reading in 1946–47 in the National War College, was included in *In the Name of Sanity* (1954).

In accordance with his own philosophy, he has sought to combine the concentration of the scholar with the broader duties of citizenship and family life. His biography of his son, killed in action in Italy at the age of 19, is entitled *Green Memories, the Story of Geddes*. This book not merely presents the portrait of a gallant youth, but it gives a picture of the rural scene around Amenia, New York, where he has written all his books since 1926.

The central themes of Lewis Mumford's life are expressed in the four books of The Renewal of Life series: *Technics and Civilization* (1934), *The Culture of Cities* (1938), *The Condition of Man* (1944), and *The Conduct of Life* (1951). Alike in the number of readers and their impact on a world audience, these are Mumford's most influential works, though his latest book, *The City in History*, has had an even wider circulation. Six half-hour films, "Lewis Mumford on the City," have been produced by the National Film Board of Canada.

Mumford's first honor came from his alma mater, City College, the Townsend Harris Medal, and the latest is the Emerson-Thoreau Medal from the American Academy of Arts and Sciences. In addition, among his major honors, he received the Gold Medal of the Town Planning Institute (Great Britain, 1957) and the Royal Gold Medal of the Royal Institute of British Architects, and the Presidential Medal of Freedom (1964). Besides being a fellow of the American Academy of Arts and Sciences, and an honorary fellow of Stanford University, Mumford is a member of the American Academy of Arts and Letters, which he served as president (1962–65), a member of the American Philosophical Society, an honorary associate of the Royal Institute of British Architects, and an honorary member of the leading architectural and planning institutes of Great Britain, Canada, and the United States. He is also a vice-president of the Société Européenne de Culture.

Like his master, Patrick Geddes, who was a biologist, sociologist, and town planner, Mumford has sought in his work to break down compartmental specialization, and to unite thought with action.

While his books cover a broad range of subjects, he achieved a special reputation as a pioneer in American studies, (*Sticks and Stones* [1924], *The Golden Day* [1926], *Herman Melville* [1929], and *The Brown Decades* [1931]), in urban history and urban design, and in the history of technology, though his popular reputation springs largely from his criticisms of modern architecture and planning. His first seven books, beginning with *The Story of Utopias* (1922), are still in print. His first book on technics, *Technics and Civilization,* a radical reinterpretation of the machine age, was supplemented by his Bamford Lectures at Columbia, "Art and Technics." He was one of the original members of the Society for the History of Technology, to whose quarterly he has been a frequent contributor. His Smithsonian lecture is a brief abstract of the theme of a third book on the same subject, as yet untitled.

Technics and the Nature of Man

LEWIS MUMFORD

THE LAST CENTURY, we all realize, has witnessed a radical transformation in the entire human environment, largely as a result of the impact of the mathematical and physical sciences upon technology. This shift from an empirical, tradition-bound technics to an experimental scientific mode has opened up such new realms as those of nuclear energy, supersonic transportation, computer intelligence, and instantaneous planetary communication.

In terms of the currently accepted picture of the relation of man to technics, our age is passing from the primeval state of man, marked by his invention of tools and weapons for the purpose of achieving mastery over the forces of nature, to a radically different condition, in which he will not only have conquered nature but detached himself completely from the organic habitat. With this new megatechnology, man will create a uniform, all-enveloping structure, designed for automatic operation. Instead of functioning actively as a tool-using animal, man will become a passive, machine-serving animal whose proper functions, if this process continue unchanged, will either be fed into a machine or strictly limited and controlled for the benefit of depersonalized collective organizations. The ultimate tendency of this development was correctly anticipated by Samuel Butler,[1] the satirist, more than a century ago: but it is only now that his playful fantasy shows many signs of becoming a far-from-playful reality.

My purpose in this paper is to question both the assumptions and the predictions upon which our commitment to the present form of technical and scientific progress, as an end itself, has been based. In particular, I find it necessary to cast doubts upon the generally accepted theories of man's basic nature which have been implicit

126

during the past century in our constant overrating of the role of tools and machines in the human economy. I shall suggest that not only was Karl Marx in error in giving the instruments of production a central place and a directive function in human development, but that even the seemingly benign interpretation by Teilhard de Chardin reads back into the whole story of man the narrow technological rationalism of our own age, and projects into the future a final state in which all the further possibilities of human development would come to an end, because nothing would be left of man's original nature, which had not been absorbed into, if not suppressed by, the technical organization of intelligence into a universal and omnipotent layer of mind.

Since the conclusions I have reached require, for their background, a large body of evidence I have been marshaling in a still unpublished book, I am aware that the following summary must, by its brevity, seem superficial and unconvincing.[2-6] At best, I can only hope to show that there are serious reasons for reconsidering the whole picture of both human and technical development upon which the present organization of Western society is based.

Now, we cannot understand the role that technics has played in human development without a deeper insight into the nature of man: yet that insight has itself been blurred, during the last century, because it has been conditioned by a social environment in which a mass of new mechanical inventions had suddenly proliferated, sweeping away many ancient processes and institutions, and altering our very conception of both human limitations and technical possibilities.

For more than a century man has been habitually defined as a tool-using animal. This definition would have seemed strange to Plato, who attributed man's rise from a primitive state as much to Marsyas and Orpheus as to Prometheus and Hephaestos, the blacksmith-god. Yet the description of man as essentially a tool-using and tool-making animal has become so firmly accepted that the mere finding of the fragments of skulls, in association with roughly shaped pebbles, as with Dr. L. S. B. Leakey's Australopithecines, is deemed sufficient to identify the creature as a protohuman, despite marked anatomical divergences from both earlier apes and men and despite the more damaging fact that a million years later no notable improvement in stone chipping had yet been made.

127

By fastening attention on the surviving stone artifacts, many anthropologists have gratuitously attributed to the shaping and using of tools the enlargement of man's higher intelligence, though the motor-sensory coordinations involved in this elementary manufacture do not demand or evoke any considerable mental acuteness. Since the sub-hominids of South Africa had a brain capacity about a third of that of *Homo sapiens,* no greater indeed than that of many apes, the capacity to make tools neither called for nor generated early man's rich cerebral equipment, as Dr. Ernst Mayr has recently pointed out.[7]

The second error in interpreting man's nature is a less pardonable one, and that is the current tendency to read back into prehistoric times modern man's own overwhelming interest in tools, machines, technical mastery. Early man's tools and weapons were common to other primates—his own teeth, nails, fists; and it was long before he could fabricate any stone tools that were functionally more efficient than these organs. The possibility of surviving without extraneous tools gave early man, I suggest, the leeway he needed to develop those nonmaterial parts of his culture which eventually greatly enriched his technology.

In treating tool-making as central to the paleolithic economy from the beginning, anthropologists have underplayed or neglected a mass of devices—less dynamic but no less ingenious and adroit—in which many other species were for long far more resourceful than man. Despite the contrary evidence put forward by R. U. Sayce,[8] C. Daryll Forde,[9] and Leroi-Gourhan,[10] there is still a Victorian tendency to give tools and machines a special status in technology and to completely neglect the equally important role of utensils. This practice overlooks the role of containers: hearths, storage pits, huts, pots, traps, baskets, bins, byres, and later, ditches, reservoirs, canals, cities. These static components play an imporatnt part in every technology, not least in our own day, with its high-tension transformers, its giant chemical retorts, its atomic reactors.

In any comprehensive definition of technics, it should be plain that many insects, birds, and mammals had made far more radical innovations in the fabrication of containers than man's ancestors had achieved in the making of tools until the emergence of *Homo sapiens:* consider their intricate nests and bowers, their beaver dams, their geometric beehives, their urbanoid anthills and termitaries. In short, if technical proficiency were alone sufficient to identify man's active intelligence, he would for long have rated as a hopeless duffer alongside many other species. The consequences of this perception should be plain: namely, that there was nothing uniquely human in early technology until it was modified by linguistic symbols, social organization, and esthetic design. At that point symbol-making leaped far ahead of tool-making, and in turn fostered neater technical facility.

At the beginning, then, I suggest that the human race had achieved no special position by reason of its tool-using or tool-making propensities alone. Or rather, man possessed one primary all-purpose tool that was more important than any later assemblage: namely, his own mind-activated body, every part of it, not just those sensory-motor activities that produced hand axes and wooden spears. To compensate for his extremely primitive working gear, early man had a much more important asset that widened his whole technical horizon: a body not specialized for any single activity, but, precisely because of its extraordinary lability and plasticity, more effective in using an increasing portion of both his external environment and his equally rich internal psychal resources.

Through man's overdeveloped, incessantly active brain, he had more mental energy to tap than he needed for survival at a purely animal level; and he was accordingly under the necessity of canalizing that energy, not just into food-getting and reproduction, but into modes of living that would convert this energy more directly and constructively into appropriate cultural—that is, symbolic—forms. Life-enhancing cultural "work" by necessity took precedence over utilitarian manual work. This wider area involved far more than the discipline of hand, muscle, and eye in making and using tools: it likewise demanded a control of all man's biological functions, including his appetites, his organs of excretion, his upsurging emotions, his widespreading sexual activities, his tormenting and tempting dreams. Even the hand was no mere horny work tool; it stroked a lover's body, held a baby close to the breast, made significant gestures, or expressed in ordered dance and shared ritual some otherwise inexpressible sentiment, about life or death, a remembered past or an anxious future. Tool-technics and our derivative machine-technics are but

129

specialized fragments of biotechnics: and by biotechnics one means man's total equipment for living.

On this interpretation one may well hold it an open question whether the standardized patterns and the repetitive order which came to play such an effective part in the development of tools from an early time on, as Robert Braidwood has pointed out, derive solely from tool-making.[11] Do they not derive quite as much, perhaps even more, from the forms of ritual, song, and dance—forms that exist in a state of perfection among primitive peoples, often in a far more exquisitely finished state than their tools. There is in fact, widespread evidence, first noted by A. M. Hocart,[12] that ritual exactitude in ceremony long preceded mechanical exactitude in work; and that even the rigorous division of labor came first through specialization in ceremonial offices. These facts may help to explain why simple peoples, who easily get bored by purely mechanical tasks that might improve their physical well-being, will nevertheless repeat a meaningful ritual over and over, often to the point of exhaustion. The debt of technics to play and to play-toys, to myth and fantasy, to magic rite and religious rote, which I called attention to in *Technics and Civilization*[13] has still to be sufficiently recognized, though Johann Huizinga, in *Homo Ludens,* has gone so far as to treat play itself as the formative element in all culture.

Tool-making in the narrow technical sense may, indeed, go back to our hominid African ancestors. But the technical equipment of Clactonian and Acheulian cultures remained extremely limited until a more richly endowed creature, with a nervous system nearer to that of *Homo sapiens* than to any primeval hominid predecessors, had come into existence, and brought into operation not alone his hands and legs, but his entire body and mind, projecting them, not just into his material equipment, but into more purely symbolic nonutilitarian forms.

In this revision of the accepted technical stereotypes, I would go even further: for I suggest that at every stage, man's technological expansions and transformations were less for the purpose of directly increasing the food supply or controlling nature than for utilizing his own immense internal resources, and expressing his latent superorganic potentialities. When not threatened by a hostile environment,

130

man's lavish, hyperactive nervous organization—still often irrational and unmanageable—was possibly an embarrassment rather than an aid to his survival. If so, his control over his psychosocial environment, through the elaboration of a common symbolic culture, was a more imperious need than control over the external environment—and, as one must infer, largely predated it and outpaced it.

On this reading, the emergence of language—a laborious culmination of man's more elementary forms of expressing and transmitting meaning—was incomparably more important to further human development than would have been the chipping of a mountain of hand axes. Beside the relatively simple coordinations required for tool using, the delicate interplay of the many organs needed for the creation of articulate speech was a far more striking advance, and must have occupied a great part of early man's time, energy, and mental concentration, since its collective product, language, was infinitely more complex and sophisticated at the dawn of civilization than the Egyptian or Mesopotamian kit of tools. For only when knowledge and practice could be stored in symbolic forms, and passed on by word of mouth from generation to generation, was it possible to keep each fresh cultural acquisition from dissolving with the passing moment or the dying generation. Then and then only did the domestication of plants and animals become possible. Need I remind you that the latter technical transformation was achieved with no better tools than the digging stick, the ax, and the mattock? The plow, like the cart-wheel, came much later as a specialized contribution to the large-scale field cultivation of grain.

To consider man as primarily a tool-making animal, then, is to skip over the main chapters of human prehistory in which a decisive development actually took place. Opposed to this tool-dominated stereotype, the present view holds that man is preeminently a mind-using, symbol-making, and self-mastering animal; and the primary locus of all his activities lies in his own organism. Until man had made something of himself, he could make little of the world around him.

In this process of self-discovery and self-transformation, technics in the narrow sense of course served man well as a subsidiary instrument, but not as the main operative agent in his development; for technics was never till our own age dissociated from the larger cultural whole, still less did technics dominate all other institutions. Early man's original development was based upon what André Varagnac[14] happily called "the technology of the body": the utilization of his highly plastic bodily capacities for the expression of his still unformed and uninformed mind, before that mind had yet achieved, through the development of symbols and images, its own more appropriate etherealized technical instruments. From the beginning the creation of significant modes of symbolic expression, rather than more effective tools, was the basis of *Homo sapiens*'s further development.

Unfortunately, so firmly were the prevailing nineteenth-century conceptions committed to the notion of man as primarily *Homo faber,* the tool-maker, rather than *Homo sapiens,* the mind-maker, that, as you know, the first discovery of the art of the Altamira caves was dismissed as a hoax, because the leading paleoethnologists would not admit that the Ice Age hunters, whose weapons and tools they had recently discovered, could have had either the leisure or the mental inclination to produce art—not crude forms, but images that showed powers of observation and abstraction of a high order.

But when we compare the carvings and paintings of the Aurignacian or Magdalenian finds with their surviving technical equipment who shall say whether it is art or technics that shows the higher development? Even the finely finished Solutrean laurel-leaf points were a gift of esthetically sensitive artisans. The classic Greek usage for "technics" makes no distinction between industrial production and art; and for the greater part of human history these aspects were inseparable, one side respecting objective conditions and functions, the other responding to subjective needs and expressing sharable feelings and meanings.[15]

Our age has not yet overcome the peculiar utilitarian bias that regards technical invention as primary, and esthetic expression as secondary or even superfluous; and this means that we have still to acknowledge that, until our own period, technics derived from the whole man in his intercourse with every part of the environment, utilizing every aptitude in himself to make the most of his own biological, ecological, and psychosocial potentials.

Even at the earliest stage, trapping and foraging called less for tools than for sharp observation of animal habits and habitats, backed by a wide experimental sampling of plants and a shrewd interpretation of the effects of various foods, medicines, and poisons upon the human organism. And in those horticultural discoveries which, if Oakes Ames[16] was right, must have preceded by many thousands of years the active domestication of plants, taste and formal beauty played a part no less than their food value; so that the earliest domesticates, other than the grains, were often valued for the color and form of their flowers, for their perfume, their texture, their spiciness, rather than merely for nourishment. Edgar Anderson has suggested that the neolithic garden, like gardens in many simpler cultures today, was probably a mixture of food plants, dye plants, medicinals, and ornamentals—all treated as equally essential for life.[17]

Similarly, some of early man's most daring technical experiments had nothing whatever to do with the mastery of the external environment: they were concerned with the anatomical modification or the superficial decoration of the human body, for sexual emphasis, self-expression, or group identification. The Abbé Breuil[18] found evidence of such practices as early as the Mousterian culture, which served equally in the development of ornament and surgery.

Plainly, tools and weapons, so far from always dominating man's technical equipment, as the stone artifacts too glibly suggest, constituted only a small part of the biotechnic assemblage; and the struggle for existence, though sometimes severe, did not engross the energy and vitality of early man, or divert him from his more central need to bring order and meaning into every part of his life. In that larger effort, ritual, dance, song, painting, carving, and above all discursive language must for long have played a decisive role.

At its point of origin, then, technics was related to the whole nature of man. Primitive technics was life-centered, not narrowly work-centered, still less production-centered or power-centered. As in all ecological complexes, a variety of human interests and purposes, along with organic needs, restrained the overgrowth of any single component. As for the greatest technical feat before our own age, the domestication of plants and animals, this advance owed almost nothing to new tools, though it necessarily encouraged the development of clay containers, to hold and preserve its agricultural abundance. But neolithic domestication owed much, we now begin to realize, since

133

Eduard Hahn and Levy,[19] to an intense subjective concentration on sexuality in all its manifestations, expressed first in religious myth and ritual, still abundantly visible in cult objects and symbolic art. Plant selection, hybridization, fertilization, manuring, seeding, castration were the products of an imaginative cultivation of sexuality, whose first evidence one finds tens of thousands of years earlier in the emphatically sexual carvings of paleolithic woman: the so-called Venuses.[20, 21]

But at the point where history, in the form of the written record, becomes visible, that life-centered economy, a true polytechnics, was challenged and in part displaced in a series of radical technical and social innovations. About five thousand years ago a monotechnics, devoted to the increase of power and wealth by the systematic organization of workaday activities in a rigidly mechanical pattern, came into existence. At this moment, a new conception of the nature of man arose, and with it a new stress upon the exploitation of physical energies, cosmic and human, apart from the processes of growth and reproduction, came to the fore. In Egypt, Osiris symbolizes the older, fecund, life-oriented technics: Atum-Re, the Sun God, who characteristically created the world out of his own semen without female cooperation, stands for the machine-centered one. The expansion of power, through ruthless human coercion and mechanical organization, took precedence over the nurture and enhancement of life.

The chief mark of this change was the construction of the first complex, high-powered machines; and therewith the beginning of a new regimen, accepted by all later civilized societies—though reluctantly by more archaic cultures—in which work at a single specialized task, segregated from other biological and social activities, not only occupied the entire day but increasingly engrossed the entire lifetime. That was the fundamental departure which, during the last few centuries, has led to the increasing mechanization and automation of all production. With the assemblage of the first collective machines, work, by its systematic dissociation from the rest of life, became a curse, a burden, a sacrifice, a form of punishment: and by reaction this new regimen soon awakened compensatory dreams of effortless affluence, emancipated not only from slavery but from work itself. These ancient dreams, first expressed in myth, but long delayed in realization, now dominate our own age.

134

The machine I refer to was never discovered in any archeological diggings for a simple reason: it was composed almost entirely of human parts. These parts were brought together in a hierarchical organization under the rule of an absolute monarch whose commands, supported by a coalition of the priesthood, the armed nobility, and the bureaucracy, secured a corpselike obedience from all the components of the machine. Let us call this archetypal collective machine—the human model for all later specialized machines—the "Megamachine." This new kind of machine was far more complex than the contemporary potter's wheel or bow-drill, and it remained the most advanced type of machine until the invention of the mechanical clock in the fourteenth century.

Only through the deliberate invention of such a high-powered machine could the colossal works of engineering that marked the Pyramid Age in both Egypt and Mesopotamia have been brought into existence, often in a single generation. This new technics came to an early climax in the Great Pyramid at Giza: that structure exhibited, as J. H. Breasted[22] pointed out, a watchmaker's standard of exact measurement. By operating as a single mechanical unit of specialized, subdivided, interlocking parts, the 100,000 men who worked on that pyramid could generate ten thousand horsepower. This human mechanism alone made it possible to raise that colossal structure with the use of only the simplest stone and copper tools—without the aid of such otherwise indispensable machines as the wheel, the wagon, the pulley, the derrick, or the winch.

Two things must be noted about this power machine because they identify it through its whole historic course down to the present. The first is that the organizers of the machine derived their power and authority from a cosmic source. The exactitude in measurement, the abstract mechanical order, the compulsive regularity of this labor machine, sprang directly from astronomical observations and abstract scientific calculations: this inflexible, predictable order, incorporated in the calendar, was then transferred to the regimentation of the human components. By a combination of divine command and ruthless military coercion, a large population was made to endure grinding poverty and forced labor at dull repetitive tasks, in order to ensure "life, prosperity, and health" for the divine or semidivine ruler and his entourage.

The second point is that the grave social defects of the human machine—then as now—were partly offset by its superb achievements in flood control, grain production, and urban building, which plainly benefited the whole community. This laid the ground for an enlargement in every area of human culture: in monumental art, in codified law, and in systematically pursued and permanently recorded thought. Such order, such collective security and abundance as were achieved in Mesopotamia and Egypt, later in India, China, in the Andean and Mayan cultures, were never surpassed until the Megamachine was reestablished in a new form in our own time. But conceptually the machine was already detached from other human functions and purposes than the increase of mechanical power and order. With mordant symbolism, the Megamachine's ultimate products in Egypt were tombs, cemeteries, and mummies, while later in Assyria and elsewhere the chief testimonial to its dehumanized efficiency was, again typically, a waste of destroyed cities and poisoned soils.

In a word, what modern economists lately termed the Machine Age had its origin, not in the eighteenth century, but at the very outset of civilization. All its salient characteristics were present from the beginning in both the means and the ends of the collective machine. So Keynes's acute prescription of "pyramid building" as an essential means of coping with the insensate productivity of a highly mechanized technology, applies both to the earliest manifestations and the present ones; for what is a space rocket but the precise dynamic equivalent, in terms of our present-day theology and cosmology, of the static Egyptian pyramid? Both are devices for securing at an extravagant cost a passage to heaven for the favored few, while incidentally maintaining equilibrium in an economic structure threatened by its own excessive productivity.

Unfortunately, though the labor-machine lent itself to vast constructive enterprises, which no small-scale community could even contemplate, much less execute, the most conspicuous result has been achieved through military machines, in colossal acts of destruction and human extermination; acts that monotonously soil the pages of history, from the rape of Sumer to the blasting of Warsaw and Hiroshima. Sooner or later, I suggest, we must have the courage to ask ourselves: Is this association of inordinate power and productivity with equally inordinate violence and destruction a purely accidental one?

Now the misuse of Megamachines would have proved intolerable had they not also brought genuine benefits to the whole community by raising the ceiling of collective human effort and aspiration. Perhaps the most dubious of these advantages, humanly speaking, was the gain in efficiency derived from concentration upon rigorously repetitive motions in work, already indeed introduced in the grinding and polishing processes of neolithic tool-making. This inured civilized man to long spans of regular work, with possibly a higher productive efficiency per unit. But the social byproduct of this new discipline was perhaps even more significant; for some of the psychological benefits hitherto confined to religious ritual were transferred to work. The monotonous repetitive tasks imposed by the Megamachine, which in a pathological form we would associate with a compulsion neurosis, nevertheless served, I suggest, like all ritual and restrictive order, to lessen anxiety and to defend the worker himself from the often demonic promptings of the unconscious, no longer held in check by the traditions and customs of the neolithic village.

In short, mechanization and regimentation, through labor-armies, military-armies, and ultimately through the derivative modes of industrial and bureaucratic organization, supplemented and increasingly replaced religious ritual as a means of coping with anxiety and promoting psychal stability in mass populations. Orderly, repetitive work provided a daily means of self-control: a moralizing agent more pervasive, more effective, more universal than either ritual or law. This hitherto unnoticed psychological contribution was possibly more important than quantitative gains in productive efficiency, for the latter too often was offset by absolute losses in war and conquest. Unfortunately the ruling classes, which claimed immunity from manual labor, were not subject to this discipline; hence, as the historic record testifies, their disordered fantasies too often found an outlet into reality through insensate acts of destruction and extermination.

Having indicated the beginnings of this process, I must regrettably pass over the actual institutional forces that have been at work during the past five thousand years and leap, all too suddenly, into the present age, in which the ancient forms of biotechnics are being either suppressed or supplanted, and in which the extravagant enlargement of the Megamachine itself has become, with increasing compulsiveness, the condition of continued scientific and technical advance. This unconditional commitment to the Megamachine is now regarded by many as the main purpose of human existence.

But if the clues I have been attempting to expose prove helpful, many aspects of the scientific and technical transformation of the last three centuries will call for reinterpretation and judicious reconsideration. For at the very least, we are now bound to explain why the whole process of technical development has become increasingly coercive, totalitarian, and—in its direct human expression—compulsive and grimly irrational, indeed downright hostile to more spontaneous manifestations of life that cannot be fed into the machine.

Before accepting the ultimate translation of all organic processes, biological functions, and human aptitudes into an externally controllable mechanical system, increasingly automatic and self-expanding, it might be well to reexamine the ideological foundations of this whole system, with its overconcentration upon centralized power and external control. Must we not, in fact, ask ourselves if the probable destination of this system is compatible with the further development of specifically human potentialities?

Consider the alternatives now before us. If man were actually, as current theory still supposes, a creature whose manufacture and manipulation of tools played the largest formative part in his development, on what valid grounds do we now propose to strip mankind of the wide variety of autonomous activities historically associated with agriculture and manufacture, leaving the residual mass of workers with only the trivial tasks of watching buttons and dials, and responding to one-way communication and remote control? If man indeed owes his intelligence mainly to his tool-making and tool-using propensities, by what logic do we now take his tools away, so that he will become a functionless, workless being, conditioned to accept only what the Megamachine offers him: an automaton within a larger system of automation, condemned to compulsory consumption, as he was once condemned to compulsory production? What in fact will be left of human life, if one autonomous function after another is either taken over by the machine or else surgically removed—perhaps genetically altered—to fit the Megamachine.

But if the present analysis of human development in relation to technics proves sound, there is an even more fundamental criticism to be made. For we must then go on to question the basic soundness of the current scientific and educational ideology, which is now pressing to shift the locus of human activity from the organic environment, the social group, and the human personality to the Megamachine, considered as the ultimate expression of human intelligence—divorced from the limitations and qualifications of organic existence. That machine-centered metaphysics invites replacement: in both its ancient Pyramid Age form and its Nuclear Age form it is obsolete. For the prodigious advance of knowledge about man's biological origins and historic development made during the last century massively undermines this dubious underdimensioned ideology, with its specious social assumptions and "moral" imperatives, upon which the imposing fabric of science and technics, since the seventeenth century, has been based.

From our present vantage point, we can see that the inventors and controllers of the Megamachine, from the Pyramid Age onward, have in fact been haunted by delusions of omniscience and omnipotence—immediate or prospective. Those original delusions have not become less irrational, now that they have at their disposal the formidable resources of exact science and a high energy technology. The Nuclear Age conceptions of absolute power, infallible computerized intelligence, limitless expanding productivity, all culminating in a system of total control exercised by a military-scientific-industrial élite, correspond to the Bronze Age conception of Divine Kingship. Such power, to succeed on its own terms, must destroy the symbiotic cooperations between all species and communities essential to man's survival and development. Both ideologies belong to the same infantile magico–religious scheme as ritual human sacrifice. As with Captain Ahab's pursuit of Moby Dick, the scientific and technical means are entirely rational, but the ultimate ends are mad.

Living organisms, we now know, can use only limited amounts of energy, as living personalities can utilize only limited quantities of knowledge and experience. "Too much" or "too little" is equally fatal to organic existence. Even too much sophisticated abstract knowledge, insulated from feeling, from moral evaluation, from historic experience, from responsible, purposeful action, can produce a serious unbalance in both the personality and the community. Organisms, societies, human persons are nothing less than delicate devices for regulating energy and putting it at the service of life.

To the extent that our Megatechnics ignores these fundamental insights into the nature of all living organisms, it is actually pre-scientific, even when not actively irrational: a dynamic agent of arrest and regression. When the implications of this weakness are taken in, a deliberate, large-scale dismantling of the Megamachine, in all its institutional forms, must surely take place, with a redistribution of power and authority to smaller units, more open to direct human control.

If technics is to be brought back again into the service of human development, the path of advance will lead, not to the further expansion of the Megamachine, but to the deliberate cultivation of all those parts of the organic environment and the human personality that have been suppressed in order to magnify the offices of the Megamachine.

The deliberate expression and fulfillment of human potentialities requires a quite different approach from that bent solely on the control of natural forces and the modification of human capabilities in order to facilitate and expand the system of control. We know now that play and sport and ritual and dream-fantasy, no less than organized work, have exercised a formative influence upon human culture, and not least upon technics. But make-believe cannot for long be a sufficient substitute for productive work: only when play and work form part of an organic cultural whole, as in Tolstoy's picture of the mowers in *Anna Karenina,* can the many-sided requirements for full human growth be satisfied. Without serious responsible work, man progressively loses his grip on reality.

Instead of liberation *from* work being the chief contribution of mechanization and automation, I would suggest that liberation *for* work, for more educative, mind-forming, self-rewarding work, on a voluntary basis, may become the most salutary contribution of a life-centered technology. This may prove an indispensable counterbalance to universal automation: partly by protecting the displaced worker from boredom and suicidal desperation, only temporarily relievable by anesthetics, sedatives, and narcotics, partly by giving wider play to constructive impulses, autonomous functions, meaningful activities.

Relieved from abject dependence upon the Megamachine, the whole world of biotechnics would then once more become open to man; and those parts of his personality that have been crippled or paralyzed by insufficient use should again come into play, with fuller energy than ever before. Automation is indeed the proper end of a purely mechanical system; and once in its place, subordinate to other human purposes, these cunning mechanisms will serve the human community no less effectively than the reflexes, the hormones, and the autonomic nervous system—nature's earliest experiment in automation—serve the human body. But autonomy, self-direction, and self-fulfillment are the proper ends of organisms; and further technical development must aim at reestablishing this vital harmony at every stage of human growth by giving play to every part of the human personality, not merely to those functions that serve the scientific and technical requirements of the Megamachine.

I realize that in opening up these difficult questions I am not in a position to provide ready-made answers, nor do I suggest that such answers will be easy to fabricate. But it is time that our present wholesale commitment to the machine, which arises largely out of our one-sided interpretation of man's early technical development, should be replaced by a fuller picture of both human nature and the technical milieu, as both have evolved together. That is the first step toward a many-sided transformation of man's self and his work and his habitat —it will probably take many centuries to effect, even after the inertia of the forces now dominant has been overcome.

REFERENCES

1. BUTLER, SAMUEL, Darwin among the machines, 1863, pp. 39–47 *in* The notebooks of Samuel Butler. Edited by H. F. Jones. London: A. C. Fifield, 1912.
2. MUMFORD, LEWIS, Science as technology. *Proc. Amer. Philos. Soc.*, vol. 105, no. 5, pp. 506–511, Oct. 1961.
3. ———, The automation of knowledge. *Audio Visual Communication Review,* vol. 12, no. 3, pp. 261–277, Autumn 1964.
4. ———, Authoritarian and democratic technics. *Technology and Culture,* vol. 5, no. 1, pp. 1–8, Winter 1964.
5. ———, Utopia, the city and the machine. *Daedalus,* vol. 94, no. 2, p. 271, Spring 1965.
6. ———, Man the finder. *Technology and Culture,* vol. 6, no. 3, pp. 375–381, Summer 1965.
7. MAYR, ERNST, Animal species and evolution, xiv + 797 pp. Cambridge, Mass.: Belknap Press of Harvard University Press, 1963.

8. SAYCE, R. U., Primitive arts and crafts, xiii + 291 pp. Cambridge, England: Cambridge University Press, 1933.
9. FORDE, C. DARYLL, Habitat, economy and society, xiv + 500 pp. London: Methuen, 1934.
10. LEROI-GOURHAN, ANDRÉ, Milieu et techniques, 512 pp., vol. 2 of Evolution et techniques. Paris: A. Michel, 1945.
11. BRAIDWOOD, ROBERT JOHN, Prehistoric men, 5th ed., 189 pp. Chicago Natural History Museum, 1961.
12. HOCART, ARTHUR MAURICE, Social origins, 153 pp. London: Watts, 1954.
13. MUMFORD, LEWIS, Technics and civilization, xi + 495 pp. New York: Harcourt, Brace, 1934.
14. VARAGNAC, ANDRÉ, Civilisation traditionnelle et genres de vie, 402 pp. Paris: A. Michel, 1948.
15. MUMFORD, LEWIS, Art and technics, 162 pp. London: Oxford University Press, 1952.
16. AMES, OAKES, Economic annuals and human cultures, 153 pp. Cambridge: Botanical Museum of Harvard University, 1939.
17. ANDERSON, EDGAR, Plants, man and life, 245 pp. Boston: Little, Brown, 1952.
18. BREUIL, HENRI, and LANTIER, RAYMOND, Les hommes de la pierre ancienne, 334 pp. Paris: Payot, 1951.
19. LEVY, GERTRUDE RACHEL, The Gate of Horn: a study of the religious conceptions of the Stone Age and their influence upon European thought. London: Faber and Faber, 1948.
20. ISAAC, ERICH, Myths, cults and livestock breeding. *Diogenes,* no. 41, pp. 70–93, Spring 1963.
21. SAUER, CARL ORTWIN, Agricultural origins and dispersals, 110 pp. New York: American Geographical Society, 1952.
22. BREASTED, JAMES HENRY, The conquest of civilization, xiv + 717 pp. New York: Harper & Bros., 1926.

ROBERT OPPENHEIMER

Robert Oppenheimer, since 1947 professor of physics and director of the Institute for Advanced Study at Princeton, N.J., was born in New York City on April 22, 1904.

At Harvard University, Oppenheimer took his B.A. degree (1926) *summa cum laude*. Having become interested in atomic physics he went abroad to study at Cambridge (1925–26) and the University of Göttingen (1926–27), where his thesis on the quantum theory earned him a Ph.D. in 1927. From 1927 to 1928 he pursued postdoctoral studies as a National Research Fellow at Harvard and the California Institute of Technology, and from 1928 to 1929 as a fellow of the International Education Board at the University of Leiden and the Technische Hochschule in Zurich.

Known for his work on the quantum theory, cosmic rays, nuclear physics, fundamental particles, and relativity, Dr. Oppenheimer also inspired others who have made significant contributions to physics while on the faculties of the University of California and the California Institute of Technology. He was first appointed in 1929 and rose from assistant professor of physics to professor and at Berkeley built up the largest school of graduate and postdoctoral study of theoretical physics in the United States. In addition to teaching, he also carried on administrative and research work at these institutions, with which he was connected until 1947.

Dr. Oppenheimer was director of the Los Alamos Science Laboratory in New Mexico from 1942 to 1945. His work there and that of thousands of others involved (from Canada and England as well as the United States) brought about the first atomic-bomb explosion on July 16, 1945. As he viewed the explosion a passage from the sacred Hindu poem, the Bhagavad-Gita (which he doubtless knew in the original, Sanskrit being his eighth language), flashed through his mind: "I am become Death, the shatterer of worlds." The creation of the bomb kept Oppenheimer busy advising the government on its use, control, and further development from October 1945, when he resigned the directorship of Los Alamos, until spring of 1947, when he became director of the Institute for Advanced Study.

From 1947 to 1953 Oppenheimer was chairman of the General Advisory Commission to the Atomic Energy Commission. In 1954 the AEC declared him a security risk and denied him further access to government secrets, although they maintained that he was a loyal citizen. Many spoke in Dr. Oppenheimer's defense, and he became a symbol of the victimization of the innocent in the McCarthy era. The bestowal of the AEC's highest honor, the Enrico Fermi Award, on Dr. Oppenheimer in December 1963 was, in addition to recognition of his contributions to theoretical physics, a symbol of the United States Government's desire to make partial amends to a loyal American.

Dr. Oppenheimer holds the Medal of Merit and several foreign orders and honorary doctorates; is a fellow of the National Research Council, American Physical Society (president, 1948), Royal Society, California Institute of Technology (1947–48), American Academy, and the Royal Danish Academy; a member of the National Academy of Sciences, American Philosophical Society, and several foreign academies, and formerly was a member of the Board of Overseers, Harvard University (1949–55). He is an honorary fellow of Christ's College, Cambridge.

Some of Dr. Oppenheimer's many lectures on atomic science and its relation to society have been collected in *Science and the Common Understanding, The Open Mind,* and *Some Reflections on Science and Culture.*

Physics and Man's Understanding

ROBERT OPPENHEIMER

WE ARE HERE to celebrate a birthday, honoring the foresight of a man, and the success of a great institution. This makes it fitting that we leave to one side the common plaints of our time: that physics is corrupted by money; microbiology and mathematics by pride, not unrelated to achievement; astrophysics and geophysics by access to novel and powerful instruments of exploration; the arts by alienation; and all by our lack of virtue. What truth there is, and there is some, to these anxieties is not for us today. We could begin with Joseph Henry, the first Secretary of this Institution, quoted by Dr. Ripley, when he explained to today's speakers what we should have in mind: "Knowledge should not be viewed as existing in isolated parts but as a whole, each portion of which throws light on the other . . . the tendency of all is to improve the human mind . . . for they all contribute to sweeten, to adorn, and to embellish life." When we think back on the prolonged and troubled debates with which the Congress moved toward accepting Smithson's bequest, establishing this Institution, we can only be moved to celebrate the extent to which it has managed to preserve and enlarge, not perhaps the unity, but the harmony between the sciences, between the arts and sciences, between nature and man, and between knowledge and practice, whose conflicts so troubled the Congress for almost two decades.

Physics has played a part in the history of the Smithsonian, as indeed it has in the history of the last five centuries. Closely related to astronomy, to mathematics, and to philosophy in its earlier years, it now has intimate relations also with all branches of science, and plays an increasingly explicit, conscious and visible role in the changing conditions of man's life. But it does not have the kind of unity which Smithson himself proclaimed in another quotation that Dr. Ripley gave us: "The particle and the planet are subject to the same laws, and what is learned of one will be known of the other." What we have seen in a great agon of this century is that the laws are indeed profoundly different; but again there is harmony between them, and, of course, consistency.

If physics has had these extended relations with science and practice, it has still maintained a kind of central heart of its own. This is because it seeks the ideas which inform the order of nature, and of what we know of nature. Countless phenomena which, from the point of view of physics, appear calculable and explicable but not central or essential, turn out to be pivots of our understanding in other sciences. No *a priori* study of physics would have been likely to explain the accidents that make the synthesis of carbon in the stars possible. Yet that has made a difference of some importance to man. Most of the miraculous findings of microbiology were not invented, and would not have been invented, by physicists, though they have played an appropriate part in helping to provide the instruments and the language for their discovery. For every science much is accident; for every science sees its ideas and order with a sharpness and depth that comes from choice, from exclusion, from its special eyes.

These centuries, from the first inspired studies in the thirteenth century of the nature of motion, to the latest journal, or even latest newspaper, have been sensed as a time of change, often painful change, of novelty and, increasingly, of rapid growth. What is written today deploring change, or welcoming it, has its parallel in almost every decade for the last 400 years, in Newton, in the dying Galileo, in John Donne: " 'Tis all in peeces, all cohaerence gone," wrote Donne in 1611:

> And new Philosophy calls all in doubt,
> The Element of fire is quite put out;
> The Sun is lost, and th'earth, and no mans wit
> Can well direct him where to looke for it.
> And freely men confesse that this world's spent,
> When in the Planets, and the Firmament
> They seeke so many new; then see that this
> Is crumbled out againe to his Atomies.
> 'Tis all in peeces, all cohaerence gone;
> All just supply, and all Relation.

But there is one very great difference. What has happened in this century in physics rivals, I think, in its technical and intellectual imaginativeness and profundity, what has happened at any time in human history. Its effects on the way we live are even more immediate and manifest than was the use of the magnet for navigation, or of electricity for communication and power; but it has not led to so great a change in man's views, of his place in the world, his function, his nature, and his destiny.

The years from the thirteenth century to the seventeenth saw the gradual acceptance of a material world no longer centered on man, or on his habitat, the gradual acceptance of an order in the heavens that could be described and comprehended, that sharply limited and circumscribed, though of course it did not eliminate, the role of God, or indeed of accident. We should ask ourselves, I think, why the views of Copernicus, the discoveries of Galileo, the understanding and syntheses of Newton, should so greatly have resonated through European society, so greatly altered the words with which men spoke of themselves and their destiny. For nothing like that has happened with Hubble's discovery of a constant in nature, an interval of time of something like 10 billion years, which characterizes the time in which galaxies double their distance from one another. Nothing like that happened with Einstein's theory of relativity, which tells us the meaning of velocity of light, or of quantum theory, which tells us of the meaning of the quantum. In more recent times, there is a similar contrast between the impact of the views of Darwin, and the almost total lack of general interest in Mendel's discovery of binomial coefficients in the populations of succeeding generations of peas, its rediscovery, its more recent beautiful deepening, with the great beginnings of the unraveling of its molecular basis.

To give some sharpness to my question, let me speak a little of a few of the high points of this century's physics. There are many: the discovery of new forms of order, and their very slow and gradual understanding, in the superfluid and superconducting states of matter; the discovery of the atomic nucleus itself, and the gradual unraveling of its properties, transmutations, and structure; the growing insight into the properties of the ordinary materials of our world, and of special ones made to serve us. But I should like to talk of three, which

147

at first sight seem to touch upon themes long irresistible to philosophers: the special theory of relativity, quantum theory, and particle physics. I should hasten to add that the third subject is open.

There is an analogy, long known to physicists, between the special theory of relativity and the quantum theory. Each is built about a constant of nature and has something to say about how that constant, in determining the laws of nature, restricts or enlarges our ability to learn about nature. I shall not speak of Einstein's theory of gravitation, which he called the general theory of relativity, largely because those parts of it which are assured and understood and, in part, checked by observation, were so clearly and indelibly described by Einstein that we are still not able to add much; and because those parts where Einstein felt some hesitation, or those others where no real test has so far been clearly at hand, those parts which deal with space in the very large or with truly strong gravitational fields, are still the province of the professional physicist and the astronomer.

As you all know, Einstein's first theory of relativity made clear an unexpected meaning of a constant of nature long ago determined by the astronomers, the velocity with which light propagates in empty space. It was Maxwell who showed that this constant was the same as that relating fundamental electric and magnetic units, and explained why this should be so, by showing that light is an electromagnetic wave. Einstein's role was to recognize that because of the universal validity of Maxwell's equation, and the independence of the velocity of light of the velocity of the source emitting it, this velocity must, itself, take on the role of what in earlier times was regarded as an infinite one, one which could not be surpassed. The corresponding limitations, the absence of absolute judgments of simultaneity at distant points, struck rather deep at all views of space and time ever held before. At the same time, they liberated physics to form new and consistent descriptions of nature and, by altering and refining Newtonian mechanics, to anticipate new interconnections of the most fundamental theoretical and practical import.

In some ways even more remarkable was the interpretation of Planck's constant, the quantum, that emerged from the development of the quantum theory of the atom, the work this time of many men, initiated in part by Einstein, in part by Bohr, and brought to an essential clarity by Bohr and his Copenhagen school. Here, again, physics was given a great liberation, the ability to understand the stability of atoms, the atomicity of matter, the regularities of chemistry, the atomic and molecular requirements for life, most of what physicists and chemists had known until the turn of the century. But here, again, it was discovered that the role of the quantum in the order of nature limited the traditional concepts of what we could learn about nature by experience. The quantum defines the irreducible roughness in the relations between a system being studied and the physical means—light, or beams of particles, or a gravitational field, for instance—that are used to study it. Because of this, there is an atomicity not only to the atoms and molecules, but to the traffic between them and the physical instruments of the laboratory; and, because of this, a complementary relation of mutual incompatability between different sorts of observations on an atomic system.

From this follow all the well-known features: the ineluctable element of chance in atomic physics based, not on our laziness, but on the laws of physics; the end of the Newtonian paradigm of the certain predictions of the future from the knowledge of the present; the element of choice in the approach to atomic observation. Yet perhaps the most important lesson is that objective—and massively and beautifully successful—science could be based on a situation in which many of the traditional features of objectivity were absent, and which taught us that for scientific progress and understanding, objectivity is more closely related to our ability to describe to one another what we have done and found, to verify or refute, than to its ontological foundation.

As for particle physics, it is an unfinished story, and what we are sure of today may not yet be ready to make its contribution to the common culture. Just from the requirement that in these new domains the general principles embodied in an understanding of the quantum and the velocity of light should still apply, it follows, as has been known for more than three decades, that atoms, or particles, or the ingredients of atoms, could not themselves, as all philosophical atomists had thought, be the permanent, unchanging elements of nature. They are created, destroyed, transmuted, but do not remain unaltered. What do remain enduring are certain abstract attributes of particles, of which the electric charge is the most familiar, and of which two other examples are known: the number of protonlike particles minus the number of their antiparticles, and the same number for electron-like particles. As for the several other abstract quantities, such as *strangeness* or *hypercharge,* and *isotopic spin* that do change, but remarkably slowly, we, I think, and I, I know, are not ready to tell philosophers of what we have made of it. This is not for lack of trying. But at the least, we have a rather unexpected alteration of the ancient atomists' answer to the problem of permanence and change. What lies ahead, we do not know. In the tumult of discovery and conjecture I have, myself, great hope; but whether we will be led, as has been so long speculated, to some further limits on what we can say about events in space and time on the scale of the very small, or whether the true shock will be far more shocking, I, at least, have an open mind. It may, though we hope not, and I believe not, be like *The Beast in the Jungle.*

But there is at least one other relatively new set of discoveries which may teach us rather deep lessons. No one was prepared for the power of the radio galaxies, or the apparently fantastic luminosity of the quasistellar objects. Some have thought that we were seeing the effects of truly strong gravitational fields; but until we understand better how such effects could lead to what is observed, until we understand better why galaxies are so much more effective in converting energy to radio emission than the sun is, or than we on earth are, this had best be left in the province of the professionals.

Now these, as other discoveries of this century, past and still to be made, find their way into our schools and become part of the language and the insight of new generations, and provide new attitudes and new analogies in looking at problems outside of physics, outside of science, as has already so largely happened with classical mechanics and with electricity. But it is clear that these discoveries, which were not easy to make, and which, to the professionals involved, brought a sense of terror as great as that which touched Newton, have clearly not changed our philosophy, either in the formal sense or in the homely one. They were unexpected and beautiful discoveries for whose general import Locke and Hume, above all Charles Peirce, and even William James could have prepared us.

I have sometimes asked myself when a discovery in science would have a large effect on beliefs which are not, and may perhaps never be, a part of science. It has seemed clear that unless the discoveries could be made intelligible they would hardly revolutionize human attitudes. But it has also seemed likely that unless they seemed relevant to some movement of the human spirit characteristic of the day, they would hardly move the human heart or deflect the philosopher's pen. I now think that it can be put more simply. These syntheses, these new discoveries which liberated physics, have all rested on the correction of some common view which was, in fact, demonstrably in error: they have all rested on a view which could not be reconciled with the experience of physics. The shock of discovering this error, and the glory of being free of it, have meant much to the practitioners. Five centuries ago the errors that physics and astronomy and mathematics were beginning to reveal were errors common to the thought, the doctrine, the very form and hope of European culture. When they were revealed, the thought of Europe was altered. The errors that relativity and quantum theory have corrected were physicists' errors, shared a little, of course, by our colleagues in related subjects.

A recent vivid example is the discovery of the nonconservation of parity. The error which this corrected was limited to a very small part of mankind. There is a still more recent example, the nonconservation of combined parity, more limited still in the number of us who could be shocked by it, not yet understood, but with hopeful, though still unpublished and unverified, indications of its possible deeper meaning.

Thus I think it is true that only at the beginnings of a science, or only in a society in which an awareness of the problems of science is extraordinarily widespread, can its discoveries start great waves of change in human culture. Just possibly if, in years ahead, other examples, other forms, other sites of life should be discovered, we would have a valid analogy to the great shock of the last century, when the anthropologists showed us the unimagined variety of human institutions. Although the nineteenth-century discoveries in biology had gone far to relate man to other forms of life, although anthropologists had revealed the unanticipated diversity of beliefs, values, and practices in different cultures, and the lack of universality of the ideals by which our own society had been nourished, although the psychologists had brought some supplement to the great religions in revealing again the universal traits of evil in all men, in fact these discoveries were to deepen and not to erode the sense of a universal human community.

If the impact of the developments in physics in this century on the general understanding of man has been restricted, quiet, and largely reserved for the young and the future, their practical consequences, along with those of all the natural and mathematical sciences, have been unrivaled in their sharpness and immediacy. Many of the papers in this symposium are addressed to this vast theme. I should like to speak of one, which is not isolated, in which, largely by accidents of history, the part of physics has been important: the new weaponry, the new situation of the nations and of war. It is still not clear in what way, or even whether, these developments will turn out to be important for human history. I should think it likely that they would be. These developments, and problems that they raise, cannot be lived out in isolation from all the others which characterize our time, but only concurrently. But they can be talked about in a certain isolation.

It is twenty years ago that men generally learned of the new weapons of a new order of destructiveness. At this time we knew and told our government, as no doubt experts in other countries knew and told theirs, that the bombs that cruelly, yet decisively, ended the second World War were, from a technical point of view, very much a beginning, not an end. We thought of some ideas about using deuterium and ordinary uranium to increase their power a thousandfold; we thought of the probable appropriateness of delivering such objects by rocket. We did not know too much about it; but within a decade rather much had been learned.

When I think back to the summer and the autumn of 1945, I remember a number of views of the future which were formulated in this country and, despite preoccupation with recovery from the terrible war, no doubt abroad. The simplest, and the only one which has been decisively refuted, was that these weapons would remain a monopoly, and thus either play very little part, or put to the test only the restraint, compassion, and fortitude of our own people and government. This was not my colleagues' view, of course, nor mine; but for a time, at least, it was that of many, including some of the very highest officers of our government.

Others pointed to the long history of warfare and talked of a defense against atomic bombs. In no meaningful sense has this characterized any period of the last two decades. As long as the armaments race continues, we will have to ask and re-ask whether adequate new defenses may be possible. They have not been. Thus, we have lived these years with a complementary and opposed dependence on preemption and deterrence.

Others, looking to past history, trying to look to the future, saw only the certain eventuality of apocalyptic war, postponed in all likelihood by the efforts of statesmanship until it was quite total. This is one forecast that history will never totally disprove. And still others, looking to the past with their eyes, and trying to penetrate the future, held, with Sir Llewellyn Woodward, that such self-defeating weapons would be put to one side, leaving the nations to war on one another with more limited means. I think that this view may be rather that we have just heard from Professor Whipple. There is some support for it in the wars of the present hour.

Yet there were quite other thoughts. Colonel Stimson wrote of *the necessary government of the whole;* and Mr. Grenville Clark then as now tried to accommodate the needs of world order with the freedom, the diversity, and the self-interest of the world's peoples; Einstein said simply that world government was the only answer. To the Acting Secretary of State the more importunate appeals led him to suggest that it was not always helpful to replace a difficult problem by an insoluble one.

Most of us recognized how central the relations with the Soviet Union would be, and, very soon, how ominous their course. Most of us recognized that with any *government of the whole* capable of serving as a vehicle for common aspirations, for expressing and advancing common interests, the extraordinary diversity of the nations and regions and peoples of the world would present hard problems. There were rich people, and there were very poor people; in any common society these inequalities would more and more become inequities, and the inequities more and more the source of grievance and of guilt. Even in that world which had long lived with the European heritage,

153

with a deep—though changing—Christian sensibility, differences of history, differences of political practice, conflicting assessments of the value and meaning of freedom, made talk of the world's community of interest rather a falsetto clarion. We did not then know, but we should have known, that in vast parts of the world, in Asia, in Africa, the first, the most powerful, the most spectacular of Europe's legacy would be the lure of technology, the pleasure of privilege, and the delights of an often synthetic nationalism. We knew that the rich could not, if they would, and perhaps would not, quickly reverse the inequities in conditions of life among peoples. We knew that for the world's future the variety of historical experience, the differences of tradition, of culture, of language and the arts, should be protected and preserved. This left very little of the idea of government of the whole; but it did leave something.

In June of 1945, before the first bomb, four of us, Arthur Compton, Fermi, Lawrence, and I, wrote, in answer to questions put to us by Colonel Stimson, the Secretary of War: "To accomplish these ends, [the rapid and in human life the least costly end of the war, and the preservation of the future peace of the world], we recommend that before the weapons are used not only Britain, but also Russia, France and China be advised that we would welcome suggestions as to how we can cooperate in making this development contribute to improved international relations." These views were endorsed by the Secretary of War's Interim Committee on Atomic Energy, though the Committee, of course, paid little attention at that moment to France, and to China. But in fact no meaningful communication was made at all: no attempt to enlist our then allies in a common responsibility and a common concern. That would have been a moment to begin to worry about what is now called "nuclear proliferation," for we and our then allies are the five powers that today have a known nuclear military program. I think that we will not be very successful in discouraging other powers from this course unless we show, by our own example and conviction, that we regard nuclear armaments as a transitory, dangerous, and degrading phase of the world's history, that before other nations could have competing armament, there is a good chance that armament will have become archaic.

In writing as we did in 1945, and then, of course, very much more later, we were not unaware of the diversity of condition, interest,

154

philosophy, and political institutions even in the great powers of the world, and certainly in the world at large. But we did know one thing from our experience before and even during the war: we knew something of the universality of the practice, language, discourse, and ethos of science. Los Alamos, and other wartime laboratories, were indeed international institutions. For years before the end of the war, those responsible for the organization of the scientific effort in this country—Vannevar Bush, James Conant, and many others—had been speaking of the hope of an international control of the new weapons, and a cooperative exploitation of the new sciences. Similar views were widely held in Britain. Sir John Anderson, who was the head of the United Kingdom Uranium Project, was persuaded of them. Most of all, Niels Bohr explored these possibilities in depth, recognizing that any such cooperation and any such control would have to rest on open access in all countries, and recognizing that this was the best guarantee against the self-delusion and the cultural and political and human abuses of societies that seal themselves off from their fellow men.

The years since the war have brought many examples of effective and fruitful international collaboration, in technology, in political economy, above all in the sciences. My own field just in the last years has been enriched by contributions of the greatest value from physicists whose countries a century ago were quite closed to the scientific tradition of Europe: Korea, Japan, China, Indochina, to name a few. We need to be grateful for the strength and beauty of this tradition, and to tremble as well as take heart in its power. These same years have also shown how modest, how fitful and inconstant, how easily overwhelmed has been the effect of these international communities on the nations and the governments.

If I recall at this celebration some notions of two decades ago, it is clearly because I believe them essential to our present and our future. For I see it as a crucial question of our time whether, in a world destined at best slowly to relieve the inequities of rich and poor, the exploitation of military technology, of national pride, of privilege will be met by the growth, in practice, in sensibility, in institutions, of a community of interest and understanding. In the discouragements of the day, good example must come to be our firmest ground for hope.

155

STEPHEN E. TOULMIN

Stephen E. Toulmin was born in London in 1922 and educated at Oundle School and King's College, Cambridge, where he read mathematics and physics. After wartime research on radar, he gained his Ph.D. in philosophy with his book *The Place of Reason in Ethics* and became a fellow of his college. During this period he was awarded the Arnold Gerstenberg studentship for research in philosophy. Later he was university lecturer in philosophy of science at Oxford, and was then appointed at an early age as professor and head of the department of philosophy at Leeds University. In 1959–60 he came to the United States as Visiting John Dewey Professor of Philosophy at Columbia University, with visiting appointments at Stanford and New York University also. He has held visiting positions in Melbourne, Australia, and at the Hebrew University and the Weitzmann Institute, Israel, and in March of 1960 he was the Powell Lecturer at the University of Indiana.

His long-standing interest in the relevance of science to the wider aspects of our culture led him, five years ago, to set up in London (for the Nuffield Foundation) a new "Unit for the History of Ideas," where he directed a program of research, books, and films on scientific ideas. In September 1965 he took up a new appointment as professor of philosophy and history of ideas at Brandeis University.

A project which took him far afield and resulted in his writing *Night Sky at Rhodes* (1963) is best described by Toulmin in his preface to that work: "During the spring of 1961, a small academic film unit was in Greece and Turkey, making a film about the beginnings of science. We had gone there with an intense interest in the scientific ideas of the classical Greeks and the conviction that, of all the aspects of Hellenic achievement, this alone was completely unique. . . . Why was this, and how did it come about? We started with these questions; and also with the feeling that, unless we could see them in relation to the life which created them, the literary relics which are our prime evidence about the first systems of scientific ideas must remain just so many words. Possibly this connection could no longer be made; the tenuous threads joining those ideas to the vanished life from which they sprang had—presumably—been snapped by history past hope and reconstruction.

"Or had they? That was what we wanted to find out . . ."

Toulmin has written and lectured extensively on philosophy and on the development of scientific thought. His most important books have been *The Philosophy of Science: An Introduction* (1953); *The Uses of Argument* (1958); *Foresight and Understanding* (1961); and (in collaboration with his wife, June Goodfield) *The Fabric of the Heavens* (1961); *The Architecture of Matter* (1962); and *The Discovery of Time* (1965).

In his preface to Toulmin's *Foresight and Understanding*, Jacques Barzun writes of him: "To know what science is, what it does, and how it affects other manifestations of mind is a task for the man who is at once critic, historian, and philosopher, and who has also been trained in one of the sciences as well as mathematics. Prof. Toulmin, who is qualified in these ways, has the added merit of being a lucid and lively writer. Whether one agrees or not with his strongly reasoned conclusions, one feels on reading him that he is advancing the cause of understanding."

Intellectual Values and the Future

STEPHEN E. TOULMIN

THE MOST REMARKABLE SINGLE FACT about the human species is this: that, having grown up *within* a natural environment, a species should have ended by *understanding* that environment. Having evolved on a planet, under a sky, surrounded by creatures of other different kinds, treading a ground containing the relics of its own forebears, the human species (and the human species alone) has achieved an intellectual command over the nature and workings of all these things. Other contributors to this symposium have challenged us to think afresh about the creative achievements of man—in the fine arts, in technology and society, and in the reconstruction of his own past—or alternatively, about the world of nature, and man's effects on that world. Let me now pull the threads of our discussion together, by focusing attention on the intellectual bond *between* man and nature and on the values by which that bond is sustained.

I emphasize understanding rather than control, intellectual command rather than practical command. What, then, are our intellectual values? How did they originate? And why does it matter so much that they should be preserved today?

The primary aim of our understanding, the primary significance of our intellectual capacities, remains the same for us now as it was in earlier times: that liberation of the mind which James Smithson's contemporaries knew by the name of "enlightenment," freeing us from superannuated routines of thought and refining our ability to respond to the realities of the natural world. Yet, during the past few years—particularly the past fifteen years—a further truth has been brought home to us, a truth which Smithson and his generation took on faith but which has now proved itself in works. It is this: that the process of intellectual growth is the salient point in all human development—in the development of society, in the development of the individual, in economic development, and in cultural development alike. I use the phrase "salient point" in Aristotle's original sense, to refer to the point from which all other growth springs, the point around which all other growth is organized. Even in the political and economic field, capital flows where there are the skills to exploit it. The under-*developed* countries are also and necessarily the under-*educated* ones. The liberation of the hand comes from the liberation of the mind. Never again can scientific theories be thought of as an ideological superstructure built upon an essentially economic foundation: rather, science and technology are becoming that very foundation themselves. As a result, "the increase and diffusion of knowledge among men" is becoming one of the first maxims of political and economic practice.

My crucial concern here, however, will be with the evolution of human understanding, considered quite apart from its technological dividends. For what is remarkable is not just the *fact* of man's understanding: just as remarkable is the *rate* at which this intellectual command has been achieved. The organic evolution of the human species occupied millions of years. The development of technology (that is, our manual capacities) has taken tens or hundreds of thousands of years. Yet the cultural evolution of our contemporary systems of thought about the world out of the mythological systems of the ancient Middle East is a process which has occupied not much more than two and a half thousand years. Even so, the process has not been continuous. Our current ideas are, predominantly, the products of two periods of 400 years—800 years in all. The first great age of intellectual growth began sometime in the sixth century B.C., and began to peter out around 150 B.C., after the time of Hipparchus and Archimedes. The second creative phase began in the late sixteenth century A.D. and has lasted up to the present time. Once this is admitted, a large question imposes itself on us: "What was so special about the state of affairs during those particular eight centuries?" What preconditions were required in the past, in order to insure the creation and continuation of vigorous intellectual traditions? And what conditions must we ourselves aim at now, if we wish to maintain healthy and self-sustaining intellectual growth within our own culture?

Two things have to be said straight away. First: we do not yet know the complete answer to these questions. Secondly: the conditions in question are, clearly, very complex. Over the past fifty years historians, philosophers, and sociologists have studied, with great care and with valuable results, the origins of modern science, the structure of intellectual systems, and the personalities and affiliations of the individuals chiefly involved in the development of our scientific tradition. But their research has been done only partly with an eye to the questions I have stated; and, as a result, the very facts on which a satisfactory answer to my questions would have to be based are in some cases still missing. Nor do we yet have any adequate general analysis of the factors involved in intellectual evolution and development. The popular theory, according to which scientific growth takes place by a sequence of thoroughgoing intellectual revolutions, tells us no more about the development of science than Georges Cuvier's geological theory, that the crust of the earth developed as a result of a corresponding sequence of catastrophic alterations. Accordingly, we lack not only the facts we need but also the explanatory concepts which would enable us to grasp the nature of the process of intellectual development in science and culture. So anything I say here by way of answering my own questions will inevitably be tentative and provisional, pending better (and better-established) insights than any we yet have.

When we try to be more specific, two first obvious questions present themselves: why, in antiquity, Greek science began when and where it did, and why it petered out when and where it did 400 years later. About the beginning of Greek science, Aristotle himself spoke quite definitely. He said: "When all the material wants of men were supplied, they turned to speculative thought as a leisure-time occupation." At first glance, this is a clear, and possible, economic theory about what is required for the health of pure science, viz: the existence of a leisured class. Yet, under scrutiny, the sharp outlines of Aristotle's answer become hazier. Living in fourth-century Athens, he could quite naturally assume that a sufficient supply of woolen cloth, olive oil, sunshine, sheeps' cheese, and figs constituted the satisfaction of all man's material wants. We, however, living in the middle of the twentieth century A.D., see the same facts from a rather different angle. Being under constant pressure ourselves to acquire additional artificial wants (for color television, say, or an electrically driven carving knife) we must, looking back at Aristotle's account of the beginning of science, regard his initial assumptions as—at best— rather endearing. His simple economic explanation thus dissolves into a psychological hypothesis. If men are to commit themselves whole-heartedly to the disinterested pursuit of knowledge, then at any rate they must not be *too* distracted by extraneous material pressures.

As for the end of scientific growth in antiquity: about that, too, much of the mystery is still unresolved. Why did the Athenian intellectual tradition never transplant, wholly and successfully, to Alexandria? Why did the intellectual impulses from which Greek science began become displaced, about 150 B.C., by technological and mystical impulses? The loss of intellectual self-confidence in Alexandria— of the original Ionian conviction that the human reason had the power to master the works of nature—that loss is a *fact*. But, like the character of Napoleon and the historical effects of Cleopatra's nose, the *explanation* of this fact remains a matter for rival theories and even for ideological debates.

Still, although my central question cannot yet be fully answered, it is at least worth attempting to produce a sketch map of the complexities involved in any general analysis of the process of intellectual growth. For several distinct groups of factors are clearly involved; and these different factors react back on one another. Some of them are economic and sociological. An intellectual tradition can grow and develop fruitfully only if men are free—and encouraged—to do three different kinds of things. They must, to begin with, be intellectually curious and fertile in novel ideas. However, novelty is not self-justifying, and so there must, in addition, be opportunities for critical debate, and for the winnowing and sifting of any new ideas put forward. And finally, the new discoveries and insights which result from this double process of innovation and criticism must be capable of being absorbed into the public mind and of taking their place in the "common sense" of the age.

Now, all these three processes—the origination of ideas, their critical assessment, and their public acceptance—are possible only given the right social contexts. For much of human history, intellectual pursuits have (economically speaking) "ridden on the back of" other professions. The astronomers of Babylon were government-paid soothsayers. The Islamic philosophers earned their living by practicing medicine. In the eighteenth century, men like Joseph Priestley and Stephen Hales were clergy by vocation, scientists by avocation. Only in the past hundred years has the pursuit of scientific knowledge become a full-time profession.

Again, for intellectual evolution to continue in a flourishing way, it is essential that heterodox ideas should be not just tolerated but positively encouraged. Let me quote, for instance, a review that appeared in 1806 of Joseph Priestley's *Memoirs,* which makes it clear to us why, around the end of the eighteenth century, effective scientific thought was possible in Britain only in the provinces. The reviewer writes: "It is a very rare felicity to meet with a man of talents outside the metropolis who does not over-rate himself and his coterie prodigiously . . . for want of *that wholesome discipline of derision* to which everything is subjected in London." Criticism is a good and necessary thing in science, but excessive, undiscriminating criticism can equally be damaging; and I have sometimes wondered whether that very quotation may not help to throw some light on James Smithson's own motivation.

Yet again; suppose one looks at the life of a nineteenth-century man from the professional classes, like Charles Darwin, and compares it with, for instance, the life of Stephen of Blois—a man of very similar temperament several centuries earlier—or with the lives of the Omnium family in the novels of Darwin's contemporary Anthony Trollope. Stephen of Blois was the kind of man who might have made a very good naturalist, but the social obligations of his time compelled him to go, very unwillingly, on the Crusades. As for the Omnium family: they were so trained to the public service that they would not have dreamt of sitting on a sofa, writing about beetles. Instead, they all went into Parliament like good, honest, God-fearing members of the ruling class. Clearly, a change of era, or even a simple change of social origin, would have destroyed Darwin's chances of working creatively and undisturbed.

163

Nor would the ideas of a Priestley or a Darwin ever have survived, or become part of our intellectual tradition, unless they had awakened some response in the wider public mind. The whole history of our culture is peppered with examples of minority groups (such as the Merton mathematicians at Oxford in the early fourteenth century) whose ideas were either lost or remained for the time being infertile, because the closed guild of men directly concerned failed to influence the broader intellectual world of their time. Taking all those social requirements together, we see just how much the intellectual health of a culture demands. A society which is tolerant of intellectual novelty, yet at the same time critical—though not *too* critical—a society in which the public mind can respond to intellectual innovations, can discriminate between them and absorb those which prove their worth: evidently this is not the kind of society which we can expect to exist everywhere and always.

Yet the social and economic conditions for intellectual growth are far from being the whole story. Psychological conditions must be right also. The attitudes of the intellectually creative groups within a society toward their own activities are just as important as the attitudes of people outside the professional groups. If one looks away from Athens to Alexandria—for instance, at Ptolemy's *Almagest*—one cannot help being struck by the tone of intellectual defeatism the author adopts toward the fundamental questions of astronomical theory. Something of the earlier doggedness of the Greek scientists, their intellectual courage and conviction, has evaporated. Above all, we miss the sense that nature is open to the mind, and that an infinitude of discoverables are waiting to declare themselves to the investigator.

Behind those psychological conditions, again, there are the deeper, philosophical axioms and attitudes of the scientist. There have been many periods—mainly, fruitful periods—in which scientists have been moved by a robust sense of a reality waiting to be studied, of nature as bringing to them an intelligible message which they only have to decipher. Yet there have been other times when the program of science has been modified, by the idea that in making scientific discoveries men are, in effect, revealing only the structure of our own minds, or that the text of the message which nature brings to us has been deliberately corrupted by a capricious deity. The equilibrium

164

between these psychological and philosophical factors is no less delicate than that involved in balancing the social and economic factors.
And in Alexandria (I suspect) all three weaknesses jointly contributed to the essential failure of intellectual nerve.

Why have I gone at such length into questions about the past? The
answer to this question must be: "For the sake of the future." We are
now at the end of the second period of 400 years' fruitful intellectual
growth, the phase which has continued triumphant and unchecked
since around 1600 and has produced the systems of ideas which we
know as modern science. Will this growth continue? Must it continue,
indeed, or might it come to a halt? If the conditions required to
preserve it are as complex as I have here suggested, maybe they will be
correspondingly difficult to maintain. Perhaps, for instance, the current transplantation of the scientific tradition from the Europe within
which it grew up to other parts of the world may produce dangers of
an Alexandrian kind. The favorable omens suggesting that science is
not only growing at the present time but growing faster than ever
before—that this is preeminently the Age of Science—are so bright as
to be dazzling. But there is a darker side to the picture, and we need to
ask ourselves from time to time whether these omens are merely
dazzling or whether they may not actually be blinding.

It is easy to believe (as I say) that the condition of science at the
present time is uniquely healthy: if only because so much of it gets
done, and because of the immense scale of the financial support which
it gets from government and industry. Yet even quantitatively the
signs are not all pointing in the optimistic direction. Ever since the
end of the seventeenth century the visible output of scientific work has
increased like compound interest. Now at last we have reached a point
beyond which the output can no longer continue to grow in the same
way. If the present pattern of growth were to continue, then fifty years
hence, on some calculations, every man, woman, and child in the
industrialized countries would have to be employed on scientific
research, and we should be having to train dolphins or computers to
do much of the work for us as well. To that extent, the very scale of
scientific growth has outgrown the possibility of its own continuance.

But these quantitative limitations are not the only dangers, and

165

perhaps not the most significant ones. For the very increases in the scale of the external support for scientific research are themselves tending to produce material pressures on the scientist similar to those which he experienced in Alexandria. In describing these pressures, I do not want to draw any cheap contrasts between pure science or applied science, or to suggest that in this context absolute purity is necessary for a state of grace. All the same, in a world in which only a certain number of Ph.D.'s can be produced, we have to recognize that the more "mission-oriented" work (to use the current inelegant jargon) is demanded, the more this will inevitably tend to weight the scale against the people whose motive for science is fundamentally a curiosity about "natural philosophy."

To mention another sign: at the present time, the scientific guilds into which the profession is organized are becoming increasingly closed, increasingly small, increasingly fragmented. A hundred years ago the list of Fellows of the Royal Society could include not only many medical practitioners but also a poet like Alfred Lord Tennyson. This, I believe, was something that was not only good for Tennyson but for the good of science also; for it helped, among other things, to maintain the channels of communication between the guilds and the public, and to match the insights of the special scientists to the capacities of the public mind. At the present time we find ourselves at the opposite extreme. The fragmentation and professionalization which Sir Kenneth Clark diagnosed in the fine arts are, if possible, even more marked in the natural sciences. We need sometimes deliberately to recall and reflect on the fact that, in many subdisciplines of natural science today, the whole living tradition of ideas—the whole master-and-pupil chain by which the ideas of the subject are transmitted—could be snapped and entirely destroyed as a result of one quite minor airplane crash.

Even among scientists themselves one can sometimes detect today a new pragmatism or loss of confidence, a flagging sense of the infinitude of discoverables. A few years back the Seaborg Report argued that the fundamental motive for a government's support of pure science must be the ambition to create "a high civilization." This year, by contrast, the scientists who prepared the National Academy of Sciences' report to Congress appeared unanimous that the final justification for the support of pure science was as an "overhead" investment necessary to support the production of technological and other dividends. And the professor of physics at Cambridge University recently went into print as saying that, in his opinion, only one more discovery would be needed to complete fundamental physics, and that the most important argument for building one new bigger (and more expensive) accelerator was to confirm that this was the last discovery. Those of us who read our history of science, in particular the late nineteenth-century debate, will wonder where we have heard this particular story before.

Up to this point I have discussed intellectual evolution in a way which has been almost entirely speculative and theoretical, as though it raised problems only for scholars. Now of course it *does* raise problems for scholars; and I myself believe that the problem of analyzing and understanding the processes of intellectual growth is one which is not only *worth* tackling in our generation but preeminently *ripe* for tackling in our generation. But, the moment one turns from considering the past and looks to the future, it is clear that the future health and growth of science and intellectual inquiry are no longer matters for theory and speculation alone—they depend acutely on how we order our affairs now, and what we decide collectively to do.

At one level, of course, governments in many countries are already aware of this, as is shown by their current conscious pursuit of what is called a "science policy." But one has also to note that the decisions involved in formulating a "science policy" always rest on assumptions about the answers to the sort of questions which I have stated. For instance, it is often said—as an axiom of policy-forming—that the "proper place" for basic research is in the universities. Yet, when I look back at the history of universities, I am forced, as a professor myself, to concede that they have *not* always been the ideal places for basic research: that they are by nature conservative, introverted, and jealous. Indeed, in the report by Dr. Haskins reprinted in the recent issues of *Daedalus,* four out of the five institutions he described as being the key centers of scientific research in our generation are not integral parts of a university at all. And probably the other implicit

167

assumptions underlying our "science policies" are equally in need of reexamining.

If we go behind these immediate policy questions, however, we have to ask not only *what* our science policies should be, but *why* we should choose as we do. We are driven back, that is, to see that questions about intellectual growth involve one, at a deeper level, in questions about the ultimate goals of national and international policy. What do we in the last resort care about? What collective enterprises are we prepared, out of sheer self-respect, to set before ourselves? In five hundred years, what do we really want our age and our culture to be remembered for?

Certainly, this age is going to be remembered as the Age of . . . something. Is it going to be the Age of Massive Technology? Is it going to be the Age of Space Exploration? Or could it perhaps be the Age of a new Scientific Renaissance? Could it perhaps be a period when, after a hundred years of increasing specialization, all aspects of our culture began to flow together once again into a new humanism— the time when, by understanding his own capacities, man's mind began both to draw strength from the knowledge of his own past, and to free itself from constraints of that past?

Certainly, at the present time, we have—and shall continue to have—massive technology, as men had in Rome and Alexandria. Certainly we have—and shall continue to have—exploration into a new world, as men had in fifteenth-century Spain. But can we hope to have, in the immediate future, a vigorous cultural renaissance as well? I doubt myself whether we can hope to have all three, unless we deliberately make that our chosen aim. And perhaps, even then, we cannot hope to achieve all three at the same time: perhaps, as they say, "something will have to give." At any rate, it is by the choices we make at this level, by the answers we give to questions of this kind, that we shall show in our own different nations and disciplines, whether we really believe that intellectual values matter—whether the example we aim to set to the rest of the world is one of mere power and productivity, or one of dignity, intellectual command, and high civilization.

Going around America with the eyes of a newcomer, I take hope from two things. In the first place, I am struck by the number of people who are clearly anxious to see this country committed to intellectual and cultural goals for their own sake: who take it for granted that the next Einstein and the next Beethoven must be Americans, and who would be quite as happy to see their country devote its energy toward trying to make this possible as they would to see that effort spent in putting a man on the moon. I take courage, too, from the fact that here, in America, you do still have a united academic world, at any rate to the extent of having a united American Academy of Arts and Sciences, in which men from many different disciplines can meet and discuss.

But I do not see only grounds for hope. Even here, a century's specialization and division have cut deep. What university, even in America, has wholeheartedly set its face against the atomization of learning, or wholeheartedly set itself to provide that common ground on which scholars from all disciplines can actively meet and match their ideas against one another? I have yet to find it. And, as for the material pressures about which I spoke earlier—the pressures for productivity, the demands for mission-oriented research—these seem to me to be, here and now, more intense than they were even in Alexandrian times.

Yet, in this regard, the special position and responsibilities of the United States cannot be denied. More than any other, this country is back in the position which Aristotle described as the necessary starting point for science: in which "all the material wants of man"—even his artificially induced wants—can be abundantly supplied. You have achieved the position John Maynard Keynes predicted thirty-five years ago in his essay on "Economic Possibilities for our Grandchildren," written at the nadir of the Great Depression. As Keynes foresaw even then, the time was coming when material production alone could no longer provide the occupations—or rather would no longer demand the labors—of a nation's entire work force. But Keynes did not see this "technological unemployment" as a threat. He saw it, rather, as a liberation and a challenge. From that time on, nations would be free to choose other collective goals, besides material productivity; and furthermore, they would *have* to choose these other goals, simply in order to occupy the creative energies of their own citizens.

If there is to be a collective public commitment in America to intellectual and cultural values for their own sake, then in this collective rededication the Smithsonian Institution will have a great part to play. For America's national commitment to intellectual and cultural values *as ends in themselves* is just what the Smithsonian has always embodied. Here science is studied preeminently as natural philosophy, with a concentration on astrophysics, natural history, archeology—branches of science whose prime significance is cultural rather than technological—and these subjects are studied alongside the humanities and the fine arts, in such a way that the different aspects of human culture necessarily interact. Again, there is scarcely an institution in the world which provides a comparable meeting point for scholars of all disciplines, and does so much to combat the fragmentation of the intellectual world. So I personally, as one who has always valued the common ground between the sciences and the humanities, have a special reason to be gratified by the invitation to contribute to this symposium. I am also delighted to say how much we applaud the ambition of the Institution's Secretary and staff to create here a new academic focus in Washington—a new advanced institute, at which scholars and scientists from all over the world can meet and exchange their ideas.

A hundred and forty years ago, James Smithson dreamed of the possibility of a democracy which would be, at one and the same time, egalitarian and cultured. In his lifetime, many Europeans were skeptical of this possibility and some, perhaps, still are. But the United States has done much to justify the faith which men like Priestley and Smithson shared; and the Smithsonian Institution will continue to play an important part in realizing their dream.

At the outset, I spoke of the remarkable fact that the human species has succeeded in understanding its own natural environment. The challenge which now faces the species is that of attempting to understand the nature of *its own understanding*. This task is a philosophical, and a sociological, and a scientific one, all at the same time. We have to ask what makes the disinterested and critical pursuit of understanding possible and fruitful; what personal attitudes and beliefs can serve to focus intellectual creativity, or to disperse it; what processes are involved in the creation and transmission of a tradition of ideas.

We walk a tightrope between insufficient confidence on the one hand—the lack of confidence which robs us of the power to engage ourselves freely in intellectual innovation—and, on the other hand, that overconfidence which deadens the impulse to ask questions: a tightrope between insufficient criticism on the one hand—the temptation to spare one's own ideas from a sufficiently savage scrutiny—and, on the other hand, that excessive criticism which can prevent a new idea from getting started at all. And, among the foremost of the conditions of healthy intellectual growth (if I may end with a hunch) is, I believe, one which is particularly appropriate to recall at a bicentennial such as this. It is the need to avoid temporal parochialism, to recognize that the problems of intellectual health and growth are the same for all men at all times, and to have the confidence that what remains to be discovered is as vast as what we have already found out.

This essay has been something in the nature of a lay sermon; so, if I may be unorthodox, I should like to close by stating my text. It comes from a book by Lawrence Durrell, in which he is reminiscing about his life on the island of Corfu.

> I am thinking, says Zarian, how nothing is ever solved finally. In every age, from every angle, we are facing the same set of natural phenomena, moonlight, death, religion, laughter, fear. We make idolatrous attempts to enclose them in a conceptual frame, and all the time they change under our very noses.
>
> To admit that, says the Count oracularly, is to admit happiness, or peace of mind, if you like. Never to imagine that any of these generalizations we make about gods or men is valid, but to cherish them because they carry in them the fallibility of our own minds.

If only we can recognize this frailty, this fallibility, that challenge will (I believe) reassure us that the inexhaustible richness of the natural world is matched by the unexhausted capacity of our own minds for further intellectual growth.

FRED L. WHIPPLE

Fred L. Whipple, director of the Smithsonian Astrophysical Observatory and professor of astronomy at Harvard University, is internationally known for his studies in astronomy. He has developed techniques for measuring photographically the speeds and decelerations of meteors, conceived the generally accepted icy-nucleus theory for comets, and done research on meteors, interplanetary dust, comets, the Moon, and other phenomena.

In the current program of the Smithsonian Astrophysical Observatory, Dr. Whipple oversees the work of more than fifty scientists engaged in the study of stellar interiors, the upper atmosphere, meteoritics, cometary astronomy, planetary research, celestial mechanics, geodesy, and related fields. He directs a program for the visual and photographic tracking of satellites under a grant from the National Aeronautics and Space Administration and is in charge of the development of an astronomical telescope to be carried in an orbiting satellite that will map about 100,000 stars in the far ultraviolet and X-ray regions of the spectrum.

Born in Red Oak, Iowa, on November 5, 1906, Dr. Whipple received his B.A. and Ph.D. degrees from the University of California. After holding various teaching and research positions at the University of California, Stanford University, and the Lick Observatory, he went to Harvard in 1931, became professor of astronomy in 1950, and served as chairman of the Department of Astronomy from 1949 until he was named director of the Smithsonian Astrophysical Observatory in 1955. He received an honorary degree from Harvard in 1945.

As a research associate for the Radio Research Laboratory of the Office of Scientific Research and Development during World War II, Whipple headed the development of the confusion reflectors used extensively by the U.S. Air Force as a radar countermeasure. He was awarded the Presidential Certificate of Merit for this work.

An active leader in a project on upper-atmospheric research by means of meteor photography, sponsored by the Bureau of Ordnance of the U.S. Navy (1946–1951), Whipple continued working on this problem with the Air Research and Development Command of the Air Force, the Office of Naval Research, the National Science Foundation, and the National Aeronautics and Space Administration.

Professor Whipple is special consultant to the Committee on Science and Astronautics of the U.S. House of Representatives and serves actively as a member and chairman of many committees and panels of the National Aeronautics and Space Administration, the National Academy of Sciences–National Research Council, the Scientific Advisory Board of the U.S. Air Force, and the National Science Foundation, and is an officer of the Committee on Space Research (COSPAR). He has been chairman of the Gordon Research Conference on the Chemistry and Physics of Space and a member of the Rocket and Satellite Research Panel, the U.S. National Advisory Committee on Aeronautics, and several editorial boards of astronomical journals. He is a member of the National Academy of Sciences, American Philosophical Society, the American Standards Association, American Astronomical Society (vice-president 1948–1950), American Academy of Arts and Sciences, American Association for the Advancement of Science, American Geophysical Union, and American Meteorological Society. He has received several honorary degrees. In 1952 he was appointed the voting representative of the United States to the International Astronomical Union, and has served on many of the Union's various commissions and been president of several.

For his discovery of six new comets, Whipple received Donahue Medals. In recognition of his leadership in meteor research he was awarded the J. Lawrence Smith Medal of the National Academy of Sciences (1949). The Presidential Award and Gold Medal for Distinguished Federal Civilian Service (1963) was given to Whipple for his outstanding achievement in conceiving and developing "an optical satellite tracking system which stood ready to track the first artificial satellite launched and has since provided valuable scientific data." It is also noteworthy that, as long ago as 1946, Whipple was the first person to propose that a "meteor bumper" be placed about a spaceship to protect space travelers from the danger of meteor punctures of a spacecraft.

Dr. Whipple is the author of *Earth, Moon and Planets* (1942, revised 1963) and some 200 scientific papers, as well as several dozen less technical articles.

174

Knowledge and Understanding of the Physical Universe as Determinants of Man's Progress

FRED L. WHIPPLE

In considering the effect of knowledge on man, I note that certain groups of thinking people today express doubt and even alarm as to the future of the human race. In the extreme they visualize man and his purpose as being deformed under the wheels of technology while nuclear missiles menace from above. Here I propose to outline some of the historical evidence that bears on this problem. In fact, I am defending James Smithson's thesis, chiseled in stone on our new Museum of History and Technology: ". . . it is in his knowledge that man has found his greatness and his happiness."

To illustrate progress in our knowledge of the physical universe I am going to tell the history of this stone in my hand—from the collection of the Smithsonian Institution. It is part of a meteorite seen to fall from the skies in western Canada on March 4, 1960. Note that as recently as 1800 the existence of such meteorite falls was denied by Western scientists. Measurements of the rubidium and strontium in this stone show that its atoms came together some 4.5×10^9 years ago, at the same time that the earth itself was formed, according to similar measurements. Less conclusive evidence indicates that the sun, the earth, and our stone all evolved by a common set of circumstances. We have reason to believe that many of the atoms in this stone were themselves made only a hundred million years earlier; hence they are only two percent older than the stone itself! Almost

175

certainly the solar system formed as the collapse of one cloud among many in a huge mass of gas and dust. Several such stellar incubators can be seen in our galaxy today. Many other stars, some of them giants as compared with the sun, probably formed in the cloud before the sun. The giants develop rapidly and the largest become exploding supernovae, manufacturing complex atoms from the basic materials, protons and neutrons. Their new atoms appear to have mixed with old as our cloud collapsed into a rotating discus to form the solar system, much as Laplace postulated in 1796.

This stone formed in the outer mantle of a minor planet or asteroid only a few hundred kilometers in diameter moving in the asteroid belt outside the earth's orbit near Mars. It was quickly heated by its short-lived radioactive atoms. After the asteroid had cooled, it was very badly shattered by a violent collision 1.5×10^9 years ago. Perhaps other minor collisions occurred before or later.

The earth meantime was melted by radioactive heating. Somehow, by processes unknown and perhaps catastrophic, the earth lost its thick original atmosphere. All our present atmosphere and oceans arose later from gases exuded from the heated interior. The new atmosphere first contained much carbon dioxide and nitrogen but almost no free oxygen; perhaps it was much like Venus's today. The earliest detectable crust solidified 3.4×10^9 years ago. Less than 700 million years afterward, life developed on the earth as single cells. Perhaps as a consequence of this emergent life or possibly for chemical reasons, the carbon in the atmosphere became largely fixed in the rocks. Solar ultraviolet light dissociated much of the water into atoms of hydrogen and oxygen. The hydrogen escaped, leaving oxygen and nitrogen as the principal constituents of our atmosphere today.

In the interval from a few hundred million years ago to 60 million years ago, when the great dinosaurs mysteriously disappeared on earth, our stone approached Mars closely enough to be thrown into an orbit crossing that of the earth. Our stone was then very much larger than the piece that fell in 1960. Encounters with dust particles in space etched away the outer diameter, perhaps for meters, at a rate of about 1 cm. every million years before it finally struck the earth in 1960. Cosmic rays were progressively more able to penetrate the center and transmute the heavier elements into various forms of argon and other atoms which we now study.

No part of such a history of any meteorite was known in 1796 when Laplace made his hypothesis—on an erroneous basis, incidentally. The nebulae he postulated as collapsing solar systems were, in fact, galaxies composed of billions of stars. Most of the history of stones such as ours was uncovered within the *past decade!* In this short interval we have gained as much scientific knowledge over all fields as in all of man's previous million years of existence (E. G. Sherburne, Jr., *Science* 149, 381, 1965). How, then, does this burgeoning of science affect man's progress? What has knowledge done for man?

Time scales are important in answering this question. I might better have illustrated scientific progress with the story of the atomic nucleus, the story of breaking the genetic code, or our marvelous feats in space. The meteoritic story, however, brings in the flow of time.

Four important time intervals are involved. Period I has lasted some 10^{10} years, possibly the age of the universe, if it is indeed a "big bang" universe. Our sun and earth developed perhaps halfway along. Period II is at least two million years, since man began to be differentiated from the primates. Period III is the few thousand years of the historical period since man invented central government, the art of writing, and processes for surplus food production. Our knowledge of this period begins with the Sumerians and the Egyptians. It constitutes one-third percent of the interval during which man has been distinguishable from the other animals. Period IV is only a few percent of the third, a few hundred years, since the beginning of the highly accelerated scientific and technological revolution. Note that man himself seems not to have evolved perceptibly during Period III. Nor should we expect measurable changes in such a brief interval. Of especial interest are the innovations in Period IV, during the present scientific revolution, as these trends bear heavily on the future.

After this long introduction I must define my terminology. For convenience I shall use the term *knowledge* in place of "knowledge and understanding of the physical universe." By *knowledge* I mean all that man has learned, not only information and the direct results of the full circuit of the scientific method, observation–theory–prediction–observation–etc., but also the broader consequences of the method in its less complete forms. I include technology, which is to science as milk is to cream. The two develop together but they *can* be separated. In knowledge I thus include developments in food production, communication, transportation, distribution, administration, the mechanics of government, and man's total know-how. I include cultural institutions, artistic development, and other lasting achievements. How then is knowledge, in the broadest sense, a determinant of man's progress? By *progress* I mean "change for the better," introducing finally the problem of values.

It is impossible here to develop a consistent value system from basic principles, if such is even possible. I shall try to judge on the basis of the individual in society. Perforce I am a biased observer, prejudiced in many ways, particularly by the value system of my own culture and of my own profession. I can, at least, note the effects of certain variants from my value system. For example, in some philosophies and religions an individual's life is taken as a process of maturation, while the physical universe is an incidental medium in which the process occurs. The individual progresses but society need not change, nor is such change relevant. In this world view the term "man's progress" has a meaning entirely different from mine. I comment only that cultures embracing such philosophies depend in fact upon the technologies of their times. Almost universally such people and their countries show keen interest in adopting the more recent technological advances. I observe that most men *act* as though they believe in the possibility of progress for mankind even though some deny the Western interpretation of the social significance in technical advances. Rare groups actually attempt to maintain the *status quo* of the technology prevalent when they adopted their dogma.

I select eight aspects of human life for which marked changes have taken place since man's earliest tangible records. These are: *world population, life span, health, physical comfort, security from predators, religion, human dignity,* and *self-expression.* Let us discuss them one by one, note the changes with time, relate the changes to the increase of man's knowledge, and attempt to evaluate the related changes.

WORLD POPULATION. Estimates place the world population increase from 5 million beginning with the New Stone Age to a quarter billion at A.D. 1, a factor of 50 times. The number doubled from A.D. 1 to 1650, again doubled in 200 years to 1850, still again in 80 years to 1930, and is now doubling in 45 years to about 1975. The world population will then become 4 billion. Note the current escalation in the rate. The governing factor in this startling population growth is self-evident: with increasing knowledge man can produce more food, store it better, and improve the distribution, to survive in greater numbers. Other factors such as longevity produced minor perturbations on the Malthusian principle, although the balancing mechanisms are quite complex in reality. Fortunately, today we see hope of population control and thus an escape from this savage principle.

Number is important, because with too few the race could be destroyed by accident. Adam and Eve are not enough. Note that a safeguard in numbers is an individual matter since progress is meaningless for men who will never exist. Perhaps with the 5 million New Stone Age men the race could have remained safe from natural disaster without increased knowledge; perhaps there is no point in a greater number of human beings. Since we are forced to assume that living is worthwhile, then the more who can survive under optimum living conditions with dignity and opportunity for self-expression, the better. From a practical viewpoint, the greater the number cooperating, the greater the potential achievements to improve man's physical welfare and to enrich his life. Greater numbers, within limits, can certainly accelerate the growth of knowledge. Excessive numbers, involving either overcrowding or the Malthusian limit, reduce the possibility of the "good life" for the individual. Within a few years most of mankind will live in cities. I estimate that the earth's surface could ultimately support more than a thousand times the present population (heaven forbid!). Expansion into space is also to be expected. But until human fecundity is controlled we cannot attain an optimum solution for human living. That this problem is receiving serious international attention is one of the encouraging signs of our times.

LIFE SPAN. The life span of early man is not well known but surely could not have exceeded a life expectancy of twenty odd years for a healthy baby. Today the corresponding life expectancy is over seventy years in the United States. Personally, I am very grateful for my recent thirty years. Since we assume that life itself is good, an increased life span is desirable, possibly even should it involve some

179

suffering or impaired vitality. Note that the lengthened life span permits more years of formal education potentially leading to greater individual maturity and productivity over a proportionally greater period. The increase of average life span is incontestably due to the growth of knowledge and is mostly of recent origin in the cultures of the highest technical achievement. Until the nature of aging is fully understood, predictions of future longevity are sheer speculation. Note, incidentally, that in case medicine should eliminate all diseases including senility, the present United States death rate by accident would limit the average life expectancy to less than 2,000 years. Suicide, by unconscious as well as by conscious intent, might well become the controlling factor in longevity.

HEALTH. Improved health is, of course, a major reason for the increase in life span. Without question modern Western man, because of his technology, is healthier and much freer from painful and incapacitating diseases than men of older cultures. It is self-evident that progress for the individual is made when a greater fraction of mankind becomes healthy rather than sickly and pain-ridden.

In discussing physical health I have by no means forgotten the highly significant and not unrelated area of mental health. Only in recent years, unfortunately, do we have any quantitative measurement of mental health in any society. Thus, it is not possible to make a valid statement with regard to secular changes in the mental health of mankind. There is strong evidence that urban life, as compared to rural life, induces mental illness today, at least in the most crowded areas of our great cities. Both overcrowding and rapid cultural changes are involved. But how to extrapolate to the past? Since mental health could be a highly significant criterion of man's progress and since it can and will be measured, we may relatively soon determine the trend of mental health with increasing technology, perhaps in a few decades. Growth of the social and behavioral sciences gives promise, at least, for corrective action in this vital area.

PHYSICAL COMFORT. To date, generally, in the society with the greater technology the average person is physically more comfortable. Whether or not comfort is a desideratum, my own observation indicates that most individuals in most societies want it. Like wealth, it may not bring happiness, but it certainly makes one's miseries easier to bear. Personally, I believe that much of the criticism of American materialism arises from the "sour grapes" attitude of the "have nots." Much of the world unrest appears to stem from the hope of better living. Many "back-to-nature" enthusiasts will also contest my viewpoint. Most, however, like Thoreau, really do not mean *nature;* they mean a park or a preserve of nature. In a park the bears beg for food rather than forage for it. In nature one feels the bite of an icy wind on his hungry body; one's bones itch with chilblains in the winter and one's skin with insect bites in the summer; one sees his baby die in his arms with no hope for help; one sees his precious food crop destroyed by hail, drought, or predators. To avoid these experiences man makes extraordinary efforts. I will not begrudge Thoreau his park or the hermit his discomforts, but, for most men, physical comfort and leisure time can free the mind for other, and I think, better things. Do not misunderstand me. I am wholeheartedly in favor of conservation. Let us preserve natural beauty and also encourage technological progress so that we can enjoy the best of both. Finally, for the record, psychological tests show that men can carry out complicated tasks better in physical comfort than in discomfort.

SECURITY FROM PREDATORS. Fear, as measured by continuous alertness to danger and quick protective reaction, is the mark of higher life forms. It is essential to survival, except for a few highly adapted species and domesticated animals. For man, fear is a vital physiological and psychological factor because of his lack of specific adaptation. Only with planning and forethought could primitive man be temporarily free from fear, and only with organization and technology can man be generally secure. Note that as late as the seventeenth century gentlemen wore swords or hired body guards. Over the period of his existence, man has become progressively safer from personal attack by other animals and even, I believe, from his human enemies.

Fear of the predator *war,* unfortunately, remains with us. But I maintain, on the basis of history to date, that war is progressively becoming less dangerous to the average individual. You need only recall Biblical accounts of the slaughter of the losers to see that the percentage death toll in modern war, although large in numbers and degrading to culture, is still much smaller than in the past. Babylon,

Jerusalem, Carthage, and many ancient cities were literally leveled to the ground, some repeatedly. In World War II 17.6 million out of the 1,133 million involved were killed by military action, only 1.6 percent of the total. This increased the normal death rate by less than ¼ over the duration of the war. The Axis countries at the same time deliberately and in cold blood murdered 5.7 million people, slightly more than their total direct military casualties. This barbarous, bestial carnage strikes a shocking blow to any hope that human nature is changing for the better. Nevertheless, the amount of murder or the percentage of casualties in warfare is not, so far as I can see, determined by the weapons available. Wars have become relatively and progressively less destructive of man and his works. The major reason is probably *specialization* in highly technological societies. War is now converging toward machine-against-machine as contrasted to man-against-man. It is not clear, alas, whether the trend will change, whether the more lethal instruments of war in the future will actually inflict greater percentage losses. I believe, or perhaps I only hope, that the nuclear explosive, because of its lethality and world-wide effects, will not become a major instrument of war. We find reassurance in the fact that Greek fire in naval warfare and poison gas have been little utilized. For each of these weapons its mutual use in fairly matched warfare would have introduced erratic factors, including the strong possibility of mutual destruction for both contestants. Possibly the same is also true of both biological and broader chemical warfare. Again we may nourish some hope for the development of effective defensive mechanisms. Perhaps, too, if wars cannot be eliminated, they can be relegated to machine-against-machine in outer space. Our best immediate counteraction to Herman Kahn's doomsday machine may be to carry out the often-suggested massive international intellectual research project—*peace.*

I cannot deal here with internally developed fears—anxieties aroused by emotional conflicts. They fall properly under the category of mental health. But it is now evident that our modern burden of external fear is trivial compared to that carried by prehistoric man and that this burden has generally decreased with time. We must credit this progress to the fact that increased knowledge has permitted larger organizations and greater organized protection.

182

RELIGION. A religion serves man in some or all of these functions: to provide social rites, to channel vital emotions, to explain nature, and to form a basis for ethics, ideals, and purpose in life.

To explain the mysteries of nature and to satisfy certain of man's unconscious needs, two of the oldest religions, the Sumerian and the Egyptian, first postulated many gods who were continuously and consciously engaged in activating the process of nature. They were the heavenly bodies or else moved these bodies about the heavens. They kept the winds blowing, provided clouds, rain, and catastrophies, and sometimes noticed human beings. As man's observations became more systematized and as his culture developed, the essence of individual gods changed and fewer were regarded as important. After perhaps two millennia the Jews were satisfied to postulate only one prime mover, a practice that has been pursued by the offshoot Christian and Islamic religions; the former, however, is monotheistic only by a formal ruse.

The god or gods of technologically advanced peoples today do not busy themselves with the detailed processes of nature but have set in motion *natural laws,* the physical laws described by scientists, to regulate these matters. Incidentally, even Descartes was still constrained by the older concept. The debt that modern science owes to the concept of divine *law* as the basis for Sumerian ethics can be traced through Judaism, Christianity, and to Calvinism, a remarkable sequence that would be fascinating to elaborate, were space available. The Christian religion now appears to be turning away from explaining nature to concentrate more on social, ethical, and spiritual functions.

The Shinto religion in Japan suffered a blow when the divine nature of the Emperor was challenged in 1945. Note that Pope Pius XII adopted a doctrine of the exploding or "big bang" universe, a modern commitment that could prove to be wrong. If life can indeed be created in the laboratory, the basis of a number of religions will be seriously weakened. Nonetheless, loss of faith in the dogma need not destroy the social and psychological aspects of church rituals. Some great religions such as those of India take the physical world for granted as a part of natural processes and thus develop no basic conflict with science.

183

The varied and important social functions of religion, its ready explanations for the mysteries of life, and even its frequent promise of escape from death are not enough to explain the depth of its emotional appeal to man and the frequent domination of the church over his every action and even his thoughts. The reason lies in a religion's ability to evoke the *religious experience,* a culturally elaborated after-image of common infantile experience.

Of his prolonged infancy a human child remembers nothing, but during this time he reacts to his environment with powerful emotions. These experiences produce unconscious effects of profound significance to his later life. When he is faced with traumatic situations and frustrations he feels an unconscious desire to return to this state. The combination of these circumstances supplies the religious impulse in the individual, channels religious dogma, and gives religion its power as a social institution.

The long period of early maturation is exceedingly beneficial to man for other reasons. During this time our young can be molded with complex behavioral patterns that are essential for adjustment to life within our social system. The child must learn to act contrary to his natural tendencies in a myriad of both trivial and important facets of behavior. As Freud discovered, in a child's struggle between the pleasure principle and reality, maturity is achieved when and if the latter wins the battle. In a number of cultures, including ours, religion provides the parent with an acceptable source of ethics, behavior patterns, taboos, ideals, and goals with which to imprint the child. It is not surprising that a clear-cut dichotomy between government and the prevailing religion is difficult to attain in some cultures. These early imprinted behavior patterns are a useful tool for government and a source of power to the church.

In many cultures, however, proper behavior patterns and ideals are established in children by reference to authority other than religious dogma. We see a strong trend in this direction currently, as knowledge reduces the areas of mystery in nature and limits the scope of the church's claim to divine revelation.

For a child who is taught to hold the church in awe and veneration, its rituals in later life bring forth the religious experience, rekindling his infantile emotions. But the equivalent experience can, in fact, both be felt and engendered in many ways, depending upon the satisfying or frustrating experiences of infancy. It can be felt as inspiration in creativity, in personal performance, or in good works. It can also, unfortunately, be felt as exultation in personal power, in sadism, and in destruction. Thus, we must tread carefully, with wisdom, love, and kindness, as we attempt to introduce more rationality into the rearing of children.

Religion as a basis for social rites can be extremely valuable both to the individual and to society even though the rites themselves may carry the marks of their barbarous origin. In great cities the church frequently isolates small communities in which the lonely individual can find his identity and establish his role by close contact with friends in communal activities. Increasing technology is now tending to destroy the small community and to lose the individual in megalopolis. The loss is real and we must face the important but soluble problem of providing proper alternatives to preserve the mental health of man with increasing urbanization.

Finally, in many religions the dogma supplies a happy answer to the omnipresent trauma of death, both the threat of death to the individual and the actual deaths of his relatives and friends. Complicated death rituals furnish psychological compensation for shattering losses. Knowledge tends to weaken the dogma and to demote the emotional value of the rituals; thus psychological alternatives must be developed and encouraged. Actually the problem is not as difficult as it sounds. Faith in immortality does not really compensate for a true loss, while the death rituals frequently cover intense and complex emotions such as relief, guilt, fear, and greed. Time, understanding friends, and new interests are true healing agents.

In summarizing the great changes that knowledge has produced in religion, we note striking progress toward rationality, specifically in the area of explaining nature. This is neither a narrow nor a superficial gain. Superstition is a cancer in the body of constructive thought. A willingness to believe unsupported dogma implies a willingness to believe anything, no matter how absurd or dangerous. Superstitious people are dupes for the whole gamut of charlatans from medicine men to demagogues.

Education of the masses reduces superstition and also, generally, the power of a religion that claims to explain nature. Thus knowledge reduces the influence of the church as a fount of ethics, behavior, and ideals. Knowledge also carries the potential for producing sounder substitutes, but the transition period is difficult. In transition the self-regulatory mechanism of child training to provide a stable social structure becomes unbalanced. Serious problems develop. One cannot qualify the result as good until the balance is reestablished and its merit demonstrated. However, codes of ethics, behavior, and ideals based on rationality rather than dogmatic religion function perfectly well in a number of societies. Our problems of transition in the West spring largely from the fact that our religion gave us the concept of law which, in turn, led to our broad application of the scientific method now challenging the presupposition that ethics must be of divine origin.

Similarly, the current explosion of technology undermines the small community unit to feed megalopolis and to submerge the individual. As Western religion concentrates its attention on its social functions it fills a need, perhaps temporary, to restore identity and purpose to the individual.

Generally, though, the mystic hold of religion on men is weakening as knowledge contracts the areas of mystery and as the religious experience is more generally explained as a natural facet of human psychology.

HUMAN DIGNITY. In ancient historical cultures a very few privileged individuals lived almost as well as today's average beneficiaries of Western technology. A high level of material comfort and opportunity for the few, however, was based upon the enslavement or the virtual enslavement of almost all the population. Note that humans tend to measure happiness in terms of expectations, which are negligible for a slave. Thus, where it was legally possible for the slave to gain wealth and to buy his way out of servitude, he did so, or otherwise escaped when he could. The desire for freedom to determine one's actions appears almost universal among men, and also among the higher animals. I suspect that it has important survival value, in the Darwinian sense. Conditioning in infancy coupled with truly enlightened paternalism can suppress this "instinct" to the degree that some, possibly many or most, can endure or even enjoy servitude.

186

Nevertheless, we see a powerful tendency away from slavery as technological and organizational advances have increased individual productivity to the extent that there can be both plenty and opportunity for all. Along with this I sense, or hope I sense, an increasing cultural guilt regarding human slavery and a worldwide pressure toward the equalization of opportunity for all, women as well as men.

Some may hold that in our modern technological society the crack of the slave whip has been replaced by the rustle of the pay check. I contest the implications of this statement and will present an example as evidence. In the Western world today it has become almost impossible to hire house servants. Good pay, free room and board, prescribed and limited working hours, social security, and other apparent attractions of the best homes provide no real competition for the impersonalized job and pay check. Why? To me the answer is clear: the higher social status of the paid workman, be it in factory, in office, or, indeed, in a commercial house-cleaning agency. But what can be the cause of this higher social status other than a fundamental desire for independence on the part of the individual? The impersonal and impartial factory has now replaced the impersonal and impartial natural environment in which man developed. The factory management is probably less capricious than nature and far less capricious than an individual human overseer not controlled by a system. Therefore, a factory job is more desirable than personal service. Here I believe we see an expression of man's desire for dignity within his social environment. To me a vitally important trend in our knowledge explosion is to provide increasing dignity to men, not only by active efforts toward providing security and equal opportunity, but also by allowing and encouraging individual choice.

SELF-EXPRESSION. Human speech is, without doubt, the most significant and the highest form of self-expression. Whitehead says that "language is the triumph of human ingenuity, surpassing even the intricacies of modern technology." We see, indeed, that language and knowledge move forward together. Writing, printing, rapid distribution of printed material, the theater, radio, and television can now carry the thoughts of some men to all other men, at least within the limits set by education, local technology, and political barriers. He who wishes to be heard can be heard, and he who wishes to listen can

187

listen. The new media of communication are effecting a social, cultural, and educational revolution as striking as the technological revolution on which it is based. The social revolution develops, in Kenneth Bowling's term, *social self-consciousness,* the ability of the individual to look at his culture objectively, from the point of view of other cultures. The effects are and will be so significant and so far reaching that one can observe today's progress only with awe and expectation.

This social, cultural, and educational revolution bears the seeds of a great flowering in self-expression. With the approaching advent of universal literacy practically everyone in the world will be able to read, hear, or see most of the great masterpieces of human creativity and wisdom, both old and new. Universal literacy and communication could develop only because of technology. Thus, knowledge begets knowledge and further separates man from the beast.

To anthropologists artistic expression is universally a major criterion of a culture's status. Anthropologists recently developed a breathtaking new look at the cavemen of 40,000 years ago when it became undeniable that they had painted the marvelous animals and scenes on the walls of the caves in France, Spain, and elsewhere. Our modern concept of primitive man changed drastically with this discovery. The opportunities for such art, however, were severely limited. So for individual self-expression in drawing, painting, sculpture, the decorative arts, the mechanic arts, and the electronic arts we find marked evidence of progress even though the level of artistry may have improved little if any. Here the opportunities are increasing daily as technology enlarges the variety of materials and techniques available while contracting the hours committed to work. Being mostly individual in their execution, these arts are particularly suited to compensate partially for the trend away from community activities. I do not feel that we have retrogressed in this area even though there was a time in Florence, Italy, when everyone was said to be an artist or an artisan. I have no real worries about man's willingness to enjoy his opportunities for creativity and for relaxation.

As for dance, technology seems to have had little effect. The settings for dance have changed and some of its significance to the community, but the dance itself remains basically unaltered. It seems to be a fundamental form of self-expression for man.

Music, on the other hand, appears to have progressed, particularly since the musical score was developed. In primitive cultures, music and dance represent an elevated state of unified community activity, where the individual can escape from loneliness in a hostile universe and can sense the fullness of living. In urban society singing and music unify community groups of various kinds, creating a feeling of kinship or intensifying mutual purpose among those involved. Thus, the role of "folk music" seems not to have changed strikingly with time or technology. Professional music, on the other hand, both in terms of composition and performance, has risen to great heights while precision recording reproduction and transmission have made the greatest music available to all, superbly performed. Such music evokes the religious experience in many and provides a haven from the stress and frustrations of life. Music has thus gained enormously by technology and perhaps has gained in its spiritual effect on the individual.

Knowledge has recently produced for man a vast and rapidly increasing variety of gainful occupations. Presumably a man works first for security and secondly to establish comfort and status, but why not for pleasure? This is now becoming increasingly possible. Not only is automation eliminating the drudgery in gaining a livelihood, but also technology is developing areas of work that depend upon creativity and self-expression. Furthermore, the wide variety permits an individual to choose the work to which he is best suited or which he prefers. No longer need a man follow his father's footsteps regardless of aptitude or interest. The possibility of greater self-expression for a man in his work represents great progress, now well underway.

CONCLUSIONS. We see that the increase of our knowledge and understanding of the physical universe has led to remarkable changes for man. It has increased and is increasing his numbers, his life span along with a much longer period of productivity, his health accompanied by greater freedom from pain, his physical comfort, his security from predators, and his individual level of personal dignity. In these facets of man's life we see as a whole marked progress, accompanied here and there by warning signals where corrective action is required. Both the good and the bad aspects intensify with the current scientific revolution, because of rapid change.

We see that man's opportunity for self-expression grows with knowledge and that he utilizes his new potentials. Religion has

189

changed markedly as knowledge has grown. Religion generally tends slowly toward rationality and has almost given up its role as a source of knowledge about nature. As knowledge shrinks the areas of mystery in the world, the mystic appeal of religious explanations lessens. Thus, the church becomes more a social institution for man than a place to worship the supernatural. Here I see evidence of great progress. In knowledge as an ideological substitute for religious dogma, there can be faith, devotion, and even solace.

The approaching state of universal literacy and the amazing technical advances in communication and transportation are now laying the foundations for world peace, because in our contracting world the growing social self-consciousness makes all countries, political groups, and cultural groups next-door neighbors. The cost of peace, however, may seem dear. A common world language appears necessary, as does a strong world police force. Nationalism in its more rampant manifestations must certainly be subdued. The strength of the central world government needed to preserve peace is not clear. I hope only that the cultural identity of individual countries or societies will not suffer in the establishment of peace. Cultural differences should be sources of interest not sources of suspicion. They could inhibit the potential plague of uniformity.

Slashing across our eight aspects of man's life, we see brilliant brush strokes of transition: the social, cultural, and educational revolution now well under way. Prominent are many problems arising from excessive numbers as megalopolis develops. Overshadowing all is the threat of the doomsday machine. Nevertheless, the force that has created so much progress, knowledge, can be used to solve the new problems it has engendered. Note that the scientific study of man, the broad field of the social and behavioral sciences, is just beginning.

As an analogy, we can compare the science of man at present to that of astronomy at the invention of the telescope. Until recently we have been studying man only with the "naked eye." We have just invented the sociopsychic telescope and have used only a few slightly improved models. For analytic tools we have only cultural arithmetic, geometry, and algebra. The calculus for man is yet to be discovered. The new view of man in the little telescope is disturbing. It destroys old illusions and shows unexpected imperfections. But it also exposes new sources of strength. Some sceptics refuse even to look into the telescope; they question that the telescope can bring us any closer to man than we are already. But greater telescopes are being designed, more critical detectors are being constructed, and more powerful analysis is being conceived. Then with the help of the newly vitalized social and behavioral sciences and with the resultant tools of social technology man can relegate the Malthusian principle to the Dark Ages, he can optimize the level of population, he can control or even eliminate megalopolis, he can attain dignity as an individual, he can identify himself in small groups where his role is both specific and important, he can nourish his unique flair for creativity, and finally he can become inspired to greater heights of self-expression.

With vastly increased knowledge comes man's growing understanding of himself as an extraordinarily interesting phenomenon of the universe. With waxing inner confidence he can revel in his irrationalities without shame, to enjoy fully his amazing heritage of physical and emotional capacities, still dealing more and more rationally with the practical realities of life.

This great Smithsonian Institution is both a reservoir of knowledge and a source of knowledge. We who are members are proud that so many of you have come to participate in our social rites on this important occasion. You will advise us and, I hope, help us after you leave. We intend to reciprocate. Together we can form a nucleus of strength for the great tasks that beckon. We must be resourceful, persistent, and daring, for the rewards to man of knowledge have no limits. Try we must, guided by Whitehead's thought, "Panic of error is the death of progress, and love of truth is its safeguard."